THE ELECTROLYTIC AND CHEMICAL POLISHING OF METALS
IN RESEARCH AND INDUSTRY

Second revised and enlarged edition

The Electrolytic and Chemical Polishing of Metals

in research and industry

by

W. J. McG. TEGART, M.Sc., Ph.D.

Formerly: Division of Tribophysics
Commonwealth Scientific and Industrial Research Organization
Australia

Now: Department of Metallurgy
University of Sheffield

PERGAMON PRESS

LONDON · OXFORD · NEW YORK · PARIS

PERGAMON PRESS LTD.
4 & 5 *Fitzroy Square, London W.1.*
Headington Hill Hall, Oxford.

PERGAMON PRESS INC.
122 *East 55th Street, New York 22, N.Y.*
1404 *New York Avenue N.W., Washington 5, D.C.*
P.O. Box 47715, Los Angeles, California.

PERGAMON PRESS S.A.R.L.
24 *Rue des Écoles, Paris V*^e.

PERGAMON PRESS G.m.b.H.
Kaiserstrasse 75, Frankfurt-am-Main.

Published by permission of the
Commonwealth Scientific and Industrial
Research Organization, Australia

First edition 1956
Second revised edition 1959

Library of Congress Card Number 59-14977

Printed in Northern Ireland at The Universities Press, Belfast

CONTENTS

v

FOREWORD

In 1937 Pierre Jacquet showed me a specimen of high purity aluminium which he had polished by a new method involving neither rubbing nor abrasives. With suspicion and disbelief I remarked: "C'est tres joli, mais est-ce que cette technique marche chaque fois?"

Some twenty years have passed since Jacquet's discovery and in this time electrolytic polishing has become a favourite technique for many of us because polished surfaces free from deformation can be obtained so easily. It is now a standard method of preparing specimens for microscopic investigation and considerable development has taken place in its industrial applications.

Although there are books and review articles on the subject, there is still a demand by industrial and scientific users for a concise and critical summary. Some years ago the continuous demand for advice on electrolytic polishing led members of this Division to write a report which was widely distributed. Mr. Tegart has now completely re-written this report for those concerned with electrolytic polishing in science and industry. This book is the outcome.

Recommendations made and advice given in the book result from the author's experience with the various solutions and methods; the majority of the "recipes" have been tested in our laboratory. I feel confident that the information in this book will be found reliable and useful.

W. Boas
Chief, Division of
Tribophysics

Melbourne,
November 1955

ACKNOWLEDGEMENTS

Grateful acknowledgement is made to my colleagues in the Division of Tribophysics for assistance in the preparation of this book. I have drawn extensively on a previous report by R. W. K. HONEYCOMBE and D. S. KEMSLEY which was subsequently revised and extended by D. S. KEMSLEY and myself. I wish to thank L. M. CLAREBROUGH and J. F. NICHOLAS who critically reviewed the manuscript and Dr. W. BOAS who encouraged publication of the material.

Further, I wish to thank Dr. R. MONDON, Dr. P. A. JACQUET, L. E. SAMUELS and the Shandon Scientific Co. Ltd. who have kindly furnished illustrations for the revised edition.

W. J. McG. TEGART

Sheffield,
February 1959

CHAPTER 1

THE MECHANISM OF ELECTROLYTIC POLISHING

1.1. INTRODUCTION

ALTHOUGH electrolytic polishing (or electropolishing as it is commonly called) is widely used in industry and research, the exact mechanism has not been established in any specific case, although a general explanation has been developed. The metal to be polished forms the anode in an electrolytic cell, and continued solution of the metal occurs in such a way that irregularities on the surface are removed and the surface becomes smooth and bright. Such behaviour is clearly a special case of more general anodic phenomena, for it is found that, depending on the conditions of operation and the solution used, a metal anode can be either etched, polished, partially passivated, or completely passivated [1].

On a macroscopic scale the contour of a machined surface may be considered as a series of hills and valleys, the depths of the valleys and the distances between the hills depending on the methods used to produce the surface. On a microscopic scale the surface is still more complex, for smaller irregularities are superimposed on the macroscopic hills and valleys. In order to produce a truly flat surface both the macroscopic and the microscopic irregularities must be removed. Thus the functions of an ideal polishing process can be distinguished as

(a) "smoothing" by elimination of the large-scale irregularities (above a micron in size) and

(b) "brightening" by removal of the smaller irregularities (down to, say, a hundredth of a micron in size).

That the functions are distinct in most anodic processes is clear from the case of etching, where considerable smoothing takes place but the surface retains a dull matt finish (or acquires one if it is initially bright). The distinguishing feature of an electropolishing process is that it combines both functions.

It is difficult to determine the exact contribution of each of these functions in any given electropolishing process for, although the

1

smoothing can be measured by studying surfaces of known profile [2, 3] or by interferometric methods [4], the brightening effect is difficult to determine quantitatively. The apparent brightness of a surface depends on the ratio of specular to diffuse reflection. This ratio in turn depends on the smoothness of the surface, since, even if the surface is brightened over its entire area, roughness on a macroscopic scale will still give rise to diffuse reflection. In view of this, the efficiency of any brightening process should always be estimated on the basis of a metallographic examination.

It is clear that any complete theory of the mechanism of electropolishing must explain both smoothing and brightening. Present theories ascribe these effects to two distinct but related processes. These are:

(a) the formation of a relatively thick viscous layer of reaction products around the anode. This layer controls the smoothing action.

(b) the formation of a thin film on the surface of the anode. This film controls the brightening action.

These processes are related to the well-known anodic phenomena of concentration overpotential and passivity [5, pp. 400, 461] so that many of the observations on the polishing process can be interpreted readily in terms of classical electrochemistry. However, the conditions for electropolishing are more restricted than those for other anodic processes, and it is necessary to consider the polishing process as a special case.

In the following discussion, a detailed description of the process of electropolishing is given, based mainly on observations on the copper/orthophosphoric acid system. This system was first described by JACQUET in 1936 [6] and, because of its apparent simplicity, it has been studied in considerable detail by a large number of workers.

1.2. OBSERVATIONS ON THE POLISHING PROCESS IN THE COPPER/ORTHOPHOSPHORIC ACID SYSTEM

1.2.1. The relation between anode potential and anode current density

Consider a cell containing a solution of orthophosphoric acid in water and having two copper electrodes. If an increasing potential from a potentiometric circuit is applied across the cell and the cell

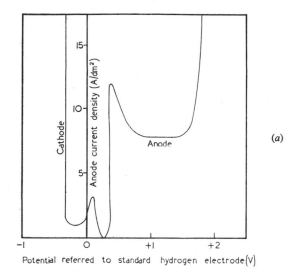

(a)

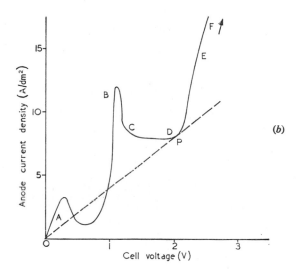

(b)

Fig. 1. Curves of anode potential, cathode potential and cell voltage as functions of anode current density for copper in 900 g/l orthophosphoric acid (potentiometric circuit). The regions on the cell voltage curve can be distinguished as:—A-B etching; B-C unstable; C-D stable plateau with polishing; D-E slow gas evolution with pitting; E-F polishing with rapid gas evolution.

P indicates optimum polishing conditions (see § 2.2).

allowed to reach equilibrium at each voltage change, then the anode potential, the cathode potential, and the voltage drop across the cell will be related to the anode current density approximately as in Fig. 1. Such curves are characteristic of those obtained in cells where a limiting current is produced by concentration overpotential. Further, the considerable drop in current from B to C is characteristic of the onset of some passivity process*. However, it is clear that there is only partial passivity since the metal still dissolves at an appreciable rate. Under such conditions of partial passivity it is not surprising that the values of voltage and current density for any given portion of the curves may vary, depending upon the manner in which the voltage is applied to the cell (although the form of these curves remains the same) [7].

Changes in the surface condition during treatment can be related to specific sections of the curves. Fig. 2 shows photomicrographs corresponding to four main stages. Along AB the specimen is etched (Fig. 2a); at BC instability occurs, and periodic oscillations of current density may occur; along CD polishing occurs at a constant current density (commonly called "limiting" current density), the quality of the polish increasing with increasing voltage up to D (Fig. 2b); along DE gas evolution occurs and the surface becomes pitted (Fig. 2c). At much higher voltages, e.g. 8–10 V across the cell, an etched and polished surface is obtained (Fig. 2d).

1.2.2. Effect of varying the conditions of electrolysis

In order to study the mechanism of the polishing process, the influence of various factors on the relation between anode potential and current density curves for copper in orthophosphoric acid has been investigated. Detailed work was carried out by HONEYCOMBE and HUGHAN [8], and their results have been supported by the further work of WALTON [9], DE SY and HAEMERS [10], HICKLING and HIGGINS [11], and ZEMBURA and MICHALIK [12].

(a) *Temperature*—HONEYCOMBE and HUGHAN [8] determined the relation between anode potential and current density at various temperatures for an electrolyte containing 522 g/l of orthophosphoric acid. At each temperature the length of the plateau was the same, but the plateau occurred at different current densities. In

---

* The relations between anode potential, anode current density, and time prior to establishment of equilibrium conditions in the region CD, are also similar to those observed in passivity studies.

each case a copper specimen was polished for 10 minutes at a voltage representing the middle point of the plateau, and the state of the surface was noted. The results are summarized in Table 1.

Table 1. *Effect of Temperature on Polishing of Copper*

Temperature (°C)	Anode potential (plateau) (V)	Current density (A/dm²)	State of surface
4·5	0·5–1·5	1·86	Good polish
22	0·5–1·5	3·88	Good polish
31	0·5–1·5	5·12	Good polish
50	0·5–1·5	8·37	Somewhat uneven
70	0·4–1·4	8·06	Uneven

HICKLING and HIGGINS [11] found little change of limiting current density for a dilute (<98 g/l) orthophosphoric acid electrolyte when the temperature was increased from 20 to 70°C. However, in more concentrated solutions the current density increased rapidly with temperature, e.g. with 784 g/l orthophosphoric acid the limiting current density at 50°C was 2·5 times its value at 20°C.

(b) *Concentration*—HONEYCOMBE and HUGHAN [8] determined the relation between anode potential and current density at room temperature for a range of concentrations of orthophosphoric acid from 65 to 1570 g/l. In all cases the plateau occurred over approximately the same range of voltage, although the current density varied with concentration. The curve of limiting current density against concentration showed a maximum at a concentration of 300 g/l. In each electrolyte, a copper specimen was polished for 10 minutes at a voltage corresponding to the middle of the plateau, and the state of the surface was noted. The results are given in Table 2.

HICKLING and HIGGINS [11] found a similar influence of concentration, and their results are summarized in Table 3. Similar results were obtained by DE SY and HAEMERS [10].

(c) *Viscosity*—The results of HICKLING and HIGGINS [11] on orthophosphoric acid solutions containing varying amounts of glycerol indicated that the limiting current density was inversely proportional to viscosity. A similar trend was shown by the results of WALTON [9]. The addition of copper phosphate to the electrolyte

Table 2. *Effect of Concentration on Polishing of Copper*

Concentration (g/l H_3PO_4)	Anode potential (plateau) (V)	Current density (A/dm²)	State of surface
65	0·3–1·3	5·27	Whole surface etched
130	0·4–1·5	9·92	Whole surface etched
196	0·5–1·4	8·68	Sign of polish on edges of specimen
261	0·6–1·5	11·63	Polishing on edges of specimen
392	0·5–1·5	5·12	Polished all over but poor at centre of specimen
522	0·5–1·5	3·88	Very good polish on entire surface
1044	0·3–1·5	1·94	Very good polish but original scratches not entirely removed
1570	0·3–1·8	0·62	Very good polish but original scratches not entirely removed

Table 3. *Influence of Concentration on Limiting Current Density*

Concentration (g/l H_3PO_4)	1176	784	392	196	98	49	9·8
Limiting c.d. (A/dm²)	1·2	4·6	13·2	17·2	15·2	9·6	2·8

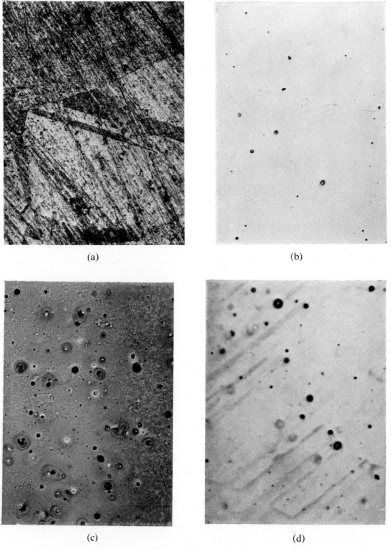

(a)

(b)

(c)

(d)

Fig. 2. Photomicrographs (×250) showing surface conditions of
α-brass specimens after anodic treatment in 900 g/l orthophosphoric acid at various voltages (potentiometric circuit).

  (a) In etching range at 0·9 V. Scratches from treatment on 600
      emery paper are still visible.
  (b) On polishing plateau at 1·4 to 1·5 V. The polished specimen
      has been lightly etched with acid ferric chloride to delineate
      grain boundaries. Pits are probably due to impurities in the
      brass.
  (c) In slow gas evolution range at 2·5 V. The presence of fine
      adherent gas bubbles produces imperfections on the surface.
  (d) In range of rapid gas evolution at 10 V. Surface is smoothed
      but etched, with imperfections due to adherent gas bubbles.

increased the viscosity and reduced the limiting current density [11, 12].

(d) *Stirring*—HICKLING and HIGGINS [11] found that mechanical stirring increased the limiting current density some 3 to 5 times. A similar trend was found by WALTON [9], namely that the specimen was polished better if it were moved through the solution at a moderate, steady speed, than if it were at rest. ZEMBURA and MICHALIK [12] found a linear relation between the limiting current density and the rotation velocity of the anode over a range from 60 to 670 r.p.m.

These observations, particularly those of (c) and (d), indicate that the electrolytic polishing of copper in orthophosphoric acid is a diffusion-controlled process.

1.2.3. The existence of a viscous layer

Microscopic examination shows that in the region of constant current density, i.e. along *CD* (Fig. 1), the surface of the anode becomes covered with a viscous layer which tends to stream off during the polishing operation. Initially, the surface of the anode may be covered with a black film, but this soon breaks up as the viscous layer is formed. During polishing, the thickness of the viscous layer remains approximately constant. More detailed microscopic examination shows that this layer is relatively thick compared to the surface irregularities, and that there is an approximately plane interface between the layer and the bulk of the solution [6, 13]. Such a layer is not observed for conditions corresponding to the region *AB* (Fig. 1) where etching occurs.

It appears that the presence of a viscous layer is intimately associated with polishing, as WALTON [9] has shown. He used a copper specimen in the form of a horizontal disk as anode, and rotated it rapidly in an orthophosphoric acid solution. When the speed of rotation was sufficiently great, only the centre of the disk was polished, while outside this area etching occurred. This was attributed to the linear velocity being so great that turbulence was set up and a viscous layer could not form. When the cell voltage was raised, thus increasing the rate of solution of the metal, the zone of polishing was extended.

The composition of the viscous layer is difficult to determine, partly because of its complex chemical nature and partly because of difficulties in sampling. In the copper/orthophosphoric acid system the results of some workers [9] indicate that the layer consists of a supersaturated solution of copper phosphate; other workers claim that it consists of phosphate hydroxide complexes [14]. Whatever the composition of the viscous layer may be, there does appear to be a correlation between the polishing properties of solutions and solubilities of the metal salts formed. For example, pyro- and orthophosphoric acids, the copper salts of which are insoluble in water but soluble in acid solution, are excellent polishing electrolytes for copper. On the other hand, metaphosphoric acid, the salts of which are insoluble in both acid and water, is useless as a polishing medium, since a thick solid film of copper salts completely passivates the anode [6].

Although the experimental results indicate that the electropolishing process is controlled by diffusion, there are two possible diffusion processes which can control the rate of electropolishing. These are: (i) the diffusion of metal ions away from the anode [9, 11], and (ii) the diffusion of acceptors, i.e. those ions or molecules with which the metal ions are combined in solution, to the anode [2, 3, 12]. At present the experimental evidence makes it difficult to decide between these, but in either case it is clear that the rate at which metal ions are removed from the surface, and hence the smoothing, depends on a diffusion process within the viscous layer.

Smoothing of a rough surface can occur if all points on the surface dissolve at a uniform rate (see, for example [2]) but measurements on surfaces of known profile [2, 3] show that smoothing during electropolishing proceeds at a greater rate than that predicted for uniform dissolution. Further, EDWARDS [3] and HICKLING and HIGGINS [11], by using composite anodes, have shown that the current density at the peaks is higher than in the valleys. On the basis of these observations, smoothing during electropolishing can be accounted for qualitatively by the differences in concentration gradient in the viscous layer over the peaks and valleys. At the peaks the layer is thin and the concentration gradient is higher while in the valleys the layer is thicker and the concentration gradient is lower. Thus preferential solution of the peaks occurs and the surface is smoothed. As yet, no really satisfactory quantitative treatment of such a smoothing process has been given.*

* WAGNER [15] has given a mathematical analysis for a smoothing process controlled by diffusion of acceptors to the anode, but similar results can be obtained without making any assumptions about the actual mechanism (see the discussion by NICHOLAS and TEGART [15]).

1.2.4. The existence of a surface film

While the concept of the viscous layer can be used to explain the smoothing process, it does not give a complete explanation of the polishing process, for the following reasons:

(a) Brightening is observed in cases where copious gas evolution occurs, e.g. at high current densities in the copper/orthophosphoric acid system. Under these conditions, a viscous layer could exert little influence.

(b) Brightening does not always occur when a viscous layer is present, e.g. PIONTELLI [16] has shown that the addition of chloride ions to various polishing solutions prevented brightening without affecting the formation of a viscous layer. The physical conditions at the metal/solution interface were apparently unchanged, but the smoothing effect alone was observed.

(c) A calculation of the resistance of an electropolishing cell shows that more than a viscous layer is involved. The work of WALTON [9] shows that the conductivity of the viscous layer in a copper/orthophosphoric acid cell is approximately 2×10^{-2} ohm^{-1} cm^{-1}. This gives the resistance of the layer as 2·5 ohm/cm^2, for a thickness of 5×10^{-2} cm. Since, however, the observed resistance for this cell varies from 10 to 23 ohm/cm^2 along the plateau, the viscous layer contributes only a tenth to a quarter of the total observed resistance.

It is therefore clear that some further factor is involved, and there is now considerable evidence suggesting that the formation of some type of film on the surface of the anode plays an important part in the polishing process. For example, HOAR and FARTHING [17] have studied the wetting of a copper surface by mercury under conditions of etching and under conditions of polishing in orthophosphoric acid. In the former case the mercury wet the surface, while in the latter it did not. They take this absence of wetting to imply the existence of a surface film, since it is well known that mercury will not wet a copper specimen that has been heated in air so as to produce a thin oxide film.

Further, periodic oscillations of current and voltage may occur in a cell before polishing conditions are established (cf. region BC of Fig. 1). In dilute electrolytes these oscillations can be maintained for long periods. From an investigation of such oscillations in a copper/

orthophosphoric acid system, MEUNIER [18] suggests that they are due to the periodic growth and destruction of a thin oxide film on the surface of the anode. Other investigators draw similar conclusions

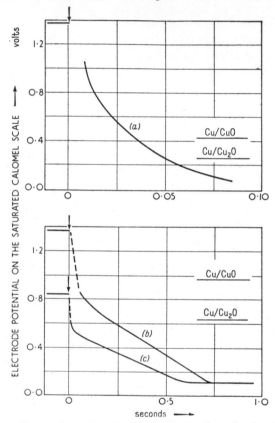

Fig. 3. Decay of anode potential for copper in orthophosphoric acid solutions when the applied voltage has been cut off after electrolysis [22]:

    (a) 764 g/l (typical polishing solution) after electrolysis for 5 min at constant c.d. of 6 A/dm²;

    (b) 49 g/l (non-polishing solution) after electrolysis for 5 min at constant c.d. of 6 A/dm²;

    (c) 49 g/l after electrolysis for 5 min at constant anode potential of 0·9 V.

Approximate values for the reversible oxide potentials are shown.

from observations on the silver/silver cyanide [19], the nickel/sulphuric acid [20] and the iron/sulphuric acid [21, 23] systems.

Direct experimental evidence for the existence of such films is difficult to obtain, since, in many cases, the film is so thin that it can be dissolved during removal of the anode from the cell. Moreover, if a film is found, it may have formed by oxidation of the polished surface on exposure to the atmosphere. Indirect evidence, however, can be obtained by studying the decay of anode potential when the applied voltage is cut off after polishing [16, 18, 22].

For the copper/orthophosphoric acid system, LAL [22] finds that the electrode potentials immediately after switching off are more positive than the reversible oxide potentials (Fig. 3). He ascribes this behaviour to a special type of surface oxide with properties different from those of a bulk oxide, and suggests that the interface consists of adsorbed oxygen and/or a thin surface oxide film. However, it is unlikely that the film always consists of oxide. For example, nickel and magnesium can be polished in solutions containing large concentrations of chloride ions which should prevent the formation of any form of oxide film, while LAL's work on the polishing of silver in a cyanide solution suggests that a film of silver cyanide forms in this case (Fig. 4).   EPELBOIN and his co-workers [4, 28] maintain that a film of adsorbed anions, e.g. ClO_4^- in perchloric acid electrolytes, exists during electropolishing.

An interesting feature of LAL's results is the distinct difference between polishing and non-polishing systems (see Figs. 3 and 4). In all the systems investigated where polishing was observed, the potential decay period was short, approximately a twentieth of a second, while in all non-polishing systems the decay period was long and varied from several seconds to minutes. On the assumption that there is a relation between the potential decay period and the thickness of film on the anode, these observations suggest that the film present during polishing is extremely thin, probably only a few atomic layers thick. Thus, it is likely that the film undergoes a continuous process involving dissolution by the electrolyte and renewal by metal from the anode. Because of its tenuous nature, such a film would dissolve readily if exposed directly to the electrolyte and it appears that a further function of the viscous layer is to assist in the maintenance of the film by restricting chemical attack [23]. Since the film is so thin, its properties need not be those of a bulk phase of the same composition, so that it is difficult to predict the characteristics of such a film.

A similar explanation has been given for the chemical passivity of certain metals. For example, if the potential of an iron, chromium, cobalt, or nickel anode in acid or neutral solution is slowly raised, a point is reached where the current falls sharply to a small value and the anodic dissolution of the metal virtually ceases. Since no

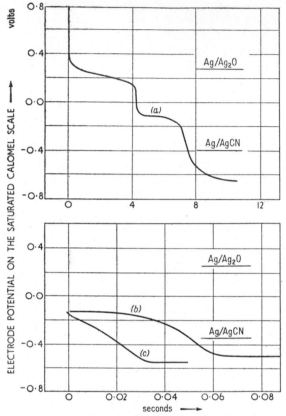

Fig. 4. Decay of anode potential for silver in 130 g/l potassium cyanide solution when the applied voltage has been cut off after electrolysis [22]:
(a) after electrolysis for 5 min at constant c.d. of 12 A/dm² (non-polishing conditions, complete passivity);
(b) after electrolysis for 5 min at constant anode potential of 0·5 V;
(c) after electrolysis for 5 min at constant anode potential of 0·0 V.
Approximate values for the reversible oxide potentials are shown.

visible change occurs at the surface of the electrode at this stage, the modern theory of passivity [1, and 5, p. 461] ascribes this change in the mode of solution to a thin transparent layer of oxide which exhibits properties completely different from those of the bulk oxide; e.g. the anodic oxide film is insoluble in acid.

The existence of a thin surface film during polishing provides an explanation for the difference between etching and brightening conditions [20, 23]. If the electrolyte has free access to the surface of the anode, etching results, because dissolution of the metal occurs preferentially from sites of high energy. In order to obtain a bright surface such preferential attack must be prevented. Although the exact role of the surface film in brightening is uncertain, a possible explanation can be suggested. The film follows the contours of the surface and is attacked uniformly by the electrolyte. Thus, in order to maintain the film, the passage of metal ions across the metal/film interface occurs at the same rate at all points. This causes brightening, for, as EDWARDS [2] has shown, such uniform removal of metal from a surface will remove irregularities.

1.3. PREDICTION OF SOLUTIONS FOR SPECIFIC METALS

Although the exact chemical reactions which occur at an anode during polishing are not yet clear, it is possible in some cases to predict solutions for a particular metal. If a limiting current density exists for a metal/solution combination, then it is probable that the solution can be developed into a suitable polishing electrolyte. A polishing solution for bismuth was developed in this way by TEGART and VINES [23]. A saturated solution of potassium iodide was chosen, since it was hoped that a film of iodide or oxyiodide would be formed on the surface of the anode and the solution of this film would be controlled by formation of $KBiI_4$. The relation between anode potential and anode current density was determined, and a typical plateau, characteristic of polishing conditions, was found. Although rapid agitation of the specimen was necessary to give polishing in this plateau region, the solution appeared promising. It is known that hydrochloric acid reacts with the oxyiodide, and by adding small quantities of this acid a more rapid dissolution of the film occurred, and a distinct improvement in finish was noted. Under these conditions, neither shaking nor stirring was necessary. The optimum composition and operating conditions are given in § 7.

CASEY and BERGERON [24] reasoned that strong basic solutions should electropolish those amphoteric metals whose oxides or hydroxides are soluble in such solutions. They considered that above some minimum current density, the concentration of metal ions X^{n+} liberated into the viscous layer would become high enough to supersaturate the layer with respect to the gelatinous $X(OH)_n$. This $X(OH)_n$ would be dissolved by the alkali metal hydroxide, MOH, to give the ions of the type XO_n^{n-}. The reaction may be expressed

$$X^{n+} + nMOH \rightarrow X(OH)_n + nM^+$$

and $$X(OH)_n + nMOH \rightarrow nM^+ + XO_n^{n-} + nH_2O.$$

However, there are indications that, at least in some cases, the primary product of the process is the oxide, subsequent conversion to the hydroxide taking place if the hydroxide is more stable. Thus those amphoteric metals which form viscous, permeable, gelatinous oxide or hydroxide films when anodized in basic solutions at practical current densities, should electropolish easily. This is the case with aluminium and zinc. Metals whose oxides or hydroxides are only slightly soluble or form impermeable and highly resistive films on the surface of the anode should not electropolish. In agreement with this, antimony, bismuth, lead, and tin cannot be polished in basic solutions [24, 25]. However, if this passivating layer could be dissolved or its structure altered in some way, these metals could possibly be electropolished. In the case of lead, attempts were made to develop a polishing solution based on a mixture of sodium hydroxide and ammonium acetate [25]. Although a bright surface was often obtained, portion of the specimen was always covered by a solid deposit beneath which no polishing had occurred. However, copper did polish in a sodium hydroxide solution containing ammonia in sufficient concentration to dissolve the copper hydroxide to form an amine complex, probably $Cu(NH_3)_4^{2+}$, [23]. The finish obtained was inferior to that obtained with orthophosphoric acid electrolytes.

Detailed consideration of the degree of hydration of ions involved in the polishing reaction in perchloric acid solutions has resulted in the development of safer solutions containing metal perchlorates rather than the acid. For example, aluminium has been polished in a magnesium perchlorate–methyl alcohol mixture, and lead in a sodium perchlorate–acetic acid mixture [4]. The development of such solutions is greatly facilitated by the use of the empirical relations developed from a study of the relation between cell resistance and cell voltage (see § 2.2).

1.4. ELECTROPOLISHING IN MOLTEN ELECTROLYTES

It was pointed out in § 1.1 that electropolishing is a special case of more general anodic phenomena, and although the discussion has been confined so far to aqueous electrolytes, there is clearly no reason why electropolishing should not occur in molten electrolytes where other anodic phenomena have been observed. However, the electrolysis of molten salts ("melts") differs from the electrolysis of aqueous solutions in many ways, e.g. the high temperatures required, the reactivity of the constituents of the system at high temperatures, and the solubility of metals in melts. Thus it is not surprising that some of the features of the polishing process are different. The recorded observations on electropolishing in melts are listed in Table 4.

The first observations were made by HOAR and MOWAT [26] on the polishing of nickel in urea-ammonium chloride melts at 120–135°C. These temperatures are not much above those recommended for polishing in some aqueous solutions, and it appears that the mechanism of polishing is very similar to that proposed for aqueous solutions. A plateau is observed on the curve of anode potential against anode current density, and this is attributed to a high concentration of nickel ions near the anode. This "layer" of nickel ions can be considered as analogous to the viscous layer in aqueous solutions. Observations further indicate that a thin compact film is formed on the anode surface and, as in aqueous solutions, this film is probably responsible for the suppression of etching.

Later, ROWLAND [27], and BROUILLET and EPELBOIN [28] studied the polishing of the precious metals in molten chlorides and fluorides at much higher temperatures (600–1000°C). In these cases it is difficult to measure single electrode potentials, and the mechanism of polishing has been studied by examining the relation between cell voltage and anode current density. However, the dissolution of deposited metal in the melt and the diffusion of metal to the anode become more marked with increased temperature, and this effect has a marked influence on the cell voltage measurements. The current density plateau becomes less distinct as the temperature increases (Fig. 5). At 1000°C there is no plateau, and the curve resembles the conventional decomposition voltage curve (Fig. 6). In order to find the optimum polishing conditions in such cases, BROUILLET and EPELBOIN [28] measured the impedance, $|Z|$ (see § 2.2). Even when there was no marked plateau of current density

Table 4. Observations on Electropolishing in Molten Electrolytes

Metal	Electrolyte	Cathode	Voltage	C.D. (A/dm²)	Time (min)	Temp. (°C)	Ref. No.	Remarks
Nickel	10–20 wt. % ammonium chloride 0·5–1·0 wt. % nickel chloride (anhydrous) Remainder urea	Nickel	2·5–3·0*	2–4	4–8	120–130	26	Definite plateaus on curves of anode voltage and cell voltage against anode current density. Melts deteriorate with time and become useless after about 3 days at temperature.
Germanium and Platinum	50 g sodium chloride 50 g potassium chloride	Platinum	1–3*		3–6	661	28	Conditions are not critical.
	52 g magnesium chloride 48 g potassium chloride	Platinum	2–3*		3–6	440		
	83 g potassium fluoride 17 g sodium fluoride	Platinum	2–4*		3–6	440		Eutectic mixture.
Palladium, Gold, and Platinum	Sodium chloride or potassium chloride	Nickel or platinum	1·5–3*	15	3–5	950–1020	27, 29	ROWLAND [27] used a Ni crucible as cathode; however, rapid corrosion occurs, and it is better to use a separate Pt cathode and a ceramic crucible. ROWLAND recommends specific temperatures and voltages for each metal, but conditions are not critical. Iron, copper, and nickel have also been treated, but the finish is poor due to attack by the electrolyte after removal from the melt.

* Approximate voltage drop across cell

there was a maximum for $|Z|$ (Fig. 5) corresponding to the optimum polishing conditions. Treatment below the voltage corresponding to $|Z|_{max}$ led to severe etching, while at higher voltages pitting occurred. Examination of the surfaces of various metals after anodic

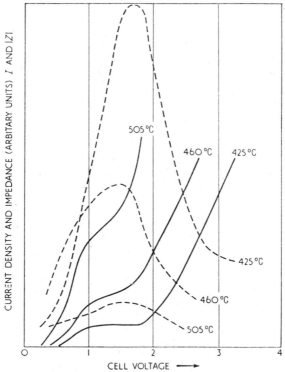

Fig. 5. Curves showing anode current density (full line) and impedance (dotted line) as functions of cell voltage for a platinum anode in molten zinc chloride at various temperatures [28].

treatment in melts at the optimum voltages shows that they are brightened and slightly smoothed, but etched at the grain boundaries. The results are thus analogous to those produced by treatment at high current densities in aqueous solutions.

From these observations, and from the work of BROUILLET and EPELBOIN on the variation of $|Z|$ for melts, it appears that the mechanism of electropolishing in melts is similar to that in aqueous solutions. However, ROWLAND [27] maintains that an explanation

in terms of a surface film on the anode is not applicable to electropolishing in melts. For example, since all the known oxides and
chlorides of platinum decompose below 600°C, in his opinion no
solid surface film can exist when platinum is brightened in sodium
or potassium chloride at 1000°C. However, as pointed out previously

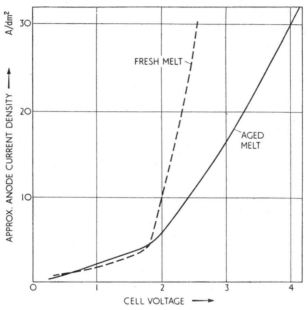

Fig. 6. Anode current density–cell voltage curves for a platinum
anode in molten sodium chloride at 1000°C. The aged melt
probably contains dissolved nickel salts derived from the nickel
crucible used.

in § 1.2.3, the conditions at the metal/electrolyte interface during
polishing cannot be described adequately in terms of the bulk
phases suspected to be present. Thus it is possible that an adsorbed
monomolecular film exists on the anode at the temperatures of
polishing. Such a film might hinder that mode of dissolution which
leads to the formation of etchpits, so that the anode becomes
brightened in a manner analogous to that already described for
aqueous solutions.

CHAPTER 2

THE ELECTRICAL CHARACTERISTICS
OF THE POLISHING PROCESS

2.1. THE RELATIONS BETWEEN ANODE POTENTIAL, CELL VOLTAGE AND ANODE CURRENT DENSITY

It is clear from Fig. 1 and the discussion of § 1.2 that the changes at the anode are the controlling factors in the polishing process, and that the relation between anode potential and anode current density should be used in any study of the mechanism. However, in practice it is usually not possible to measure anode potentials directly, so that the relation between cell voltage and anode current density has to be used to control the process and in some cases to

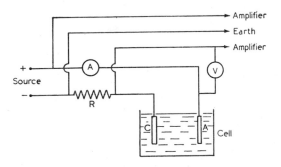

Fig. 7. Circuit used for studying cell voltage–anode current density relations with an oscillograph [40]. $R = 1$ to 5 Ω.

study the mechanism. A simple apparatus for these purposes is shown in Fig. 7. In many cases where a limiting current density is observed the results obtained with such an apparatus give a sufficient guide to operating conditions. In these cases, the potential drop through the solution is comparatively small, and the curves of cell voltage against anode current density exhibit similar characteristics to the anode potential curves. However, in other cases, e.g. in some perchloric acid solutions, the potential drop through the solution is quite large, approximately 20 to 30 V, while the anode potential is only 3 to 4 V [23], so that changes at the anode are not readily distinguished when only the overall cell voltage is considered.

The relation between cell voltage and anode current density is dependent upon the potential drop across the cell, and considerable confusion has developed through the use of two types of circuit to control the polishing process, viz. potentiometric and series circuits. Because of this confusion a false distinction is sometimes made between two forms of the curve of cell voltage against anode current density. Curves of the form shown in Fig. 1 are usually obtained with solutions when a small potential drop occurs across the cell

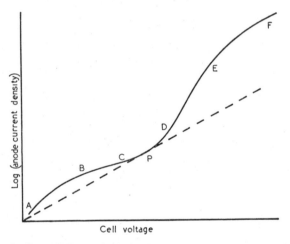

Fig. 8. General form of relation between cell voltage and anode current density when a series circuit is used. Regions can be related to anodic processes as:—A-B etching; B-C instability; C-D polishing; D-E slow gas evolution with pitting; E-F polishing with rapid gas evolution. P indicates optimum polishing conditions (see § 2.2).

and a potentiometric circuit is used; curves of the form shown in Fig. 8 are usually obtained with solutions where a large potential drop occurs across the cell and a series circuit is used. In the latter case, the limiting current plateau is almost completely absent.

The differences between the two sets of results are readily explained when the respective circuits are considered in detail (see Fig. 9, where the essential features of each are listed) and it is realized that there is complete equivalence between the two circuits. By using THEVENIN's Theorem [30] any potentiometric circuit can be replaced by an equivalent series circuit, and vice versa. For example, the two circuits illustrated in Fig. 9 have equivalent electrical characteristics, provided that the following relationships hold:

$$E' = E \cdot \frac{R_1}{R_1 + R_2}$$

and

$$R = \frac{R_1 R_2}{R_1 + R_2}.$$

A typical potentiometric circuit used for electropolishing copper in orthophosphoric acid would have values of $E = 6$ V, $R_1 = 2\ \Omega$,

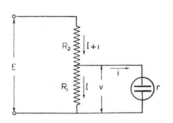 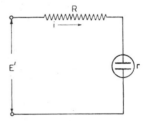

Fig. 9. Comparison of potentiometric and series circuits.

	Potentiometric	Series
Circuit equations	$v = IR_1 = ir$ $E = (I + i)R_2 + v$	$E' = (R + r)i$
Resistance relationship for optimum polishing	$R_1 \ll r$ i.e. $I \gg i$	$R \gg r$
Power loss	$(I + i)^2 R_2 + I^2 R_1$ $\simeq I^2(R_1 + R_2)$	$i^2 R$

$R_2 = 8\ \Omega$ and the equivalent series circuit would consist of a battery $E' = 1 \cdot 2$ V and a resistance $R = 1 \cdot 6\ \Omega$. It should be noted that a given potentiometric circuit has a unique series equivalent, but not vice versa, so that for a typical series circuit where $E' = 50$ V, $R = 200\ \Omega$, one equivalent potentiometric circuit is $E = 100$ V, $R_1 = R_2 = 400\ \Omega$. However, provided that the relations $\frac{R_1 R_2}{R_1 + R_2} = 200$ and $E = E' \cdot \frac{R_1 + R_2}{R_1}$ hold, a wide range of values can be chosen.

Practical potentiometric circuits are equivalent to series circuits having very low resistances, so that the current is determined mainly by the resistance of the cell, whilst the voltage across the cell remains substantially constant for all conditions, i.e. in these cases

$$R \ll r$$

and
$$v = \frac{r}{r + R} \cdot E' \simeq E'.$$

This is clearly the reason why VERNON and STROUD [31] have recommended that, for optimum operation of a potentiometric circuit, the resistance R_1 of the section of the potentiometer in parallel with' the cell should be small in comparison with the cell resistance (r). Any increase in cell resistance, as at the onset of polishing, is accompanied by an immediate fall in current, and this affords a sensitive indication of changes in the cell.

On the other hand, series circuits usually have a high series resistance compared to the cell resistance, and consequently the current is determined mainly by the series resistance and is not affected by variations in cell resistance. The voltage across the cell will vary as the resistance of the cell varies, and will be approximately proportional to the cell resistance, i.e.

$$v = ir$$

and
$$i = \frac{E'}{R + r} \simeq \frac{E'}{R} \quad \text{if} \quad R \gg r$$

$$\simeq \text{constant.}$$

Thus, by suitable variation of the electrical conditions, it is possible to obtain a range of curves of cell voltage against anode current density ranging from the case where a definite limiting current plateau is present to the case where it is completely absent.

2.2. THE RELATION BETWEEN CELL RESISTANCE AND CELL VOLTAGE

Since the formation of the layers of reaction products at the anode increases the resistance of the cell, the relation between cell resistance and cell voltage can be used to study the mechanism of polishing. For most metal/electrolyte combinations, the curve of cell resistance against cell voltage has a single maximum, corresponding to the optimum operating conditions. The position of this maximum cell resistance can be determined from the curve of cell voltage against anode current density by drawing a tangent to the curve from the origin (as shown in Fig. 1). The voltage corresponding to the maximum cell resistance depends on the type of circuit used. With a potentiometric circuit, the maximum cell resistance corresponds to the end of the polishing plateau, but with a series circuit the position of the maximum cell resistance is not so clearly defined (see Figs. 1 and 8). The maximum cell resistance can be determined readily in the laboratory using a Wheatstone bridge circuit such as that shown in Fig. 10 [32]. A refinement involves

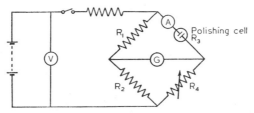

Fig. 10. Wheatstone bridge circuit used for the control of electropolishing in the laboratory [32]. The ratio R_2/R_1 is chosen to make R_4 small compared with R_3 (the cell resistance).

the use of a cathode ray oscillograph and a relay circuit adjusted to keep the cell voltage at the optimum value [33].

With ferrous alloys in solutions of the chromic acid–acetic acid type, polishing can occur in a voltage range where no maximum is observed on the curve of cell resistance against cell voltage [29]. Further, EPELBOIN [34] has found that solutions containing chromate ions do not have distinct maxima so that the bridge-type control circuit cannot be applied successfully to these solutions.

EPELBOIN and his co-workers [4, 28, 34] have used a very high frequency a.c. technique to measure the impedance of an electropolishing cell. By using a modified Wheatstone bridge circuit, they measured simultaneously the variation of the apparent resistance (V/I) and the impedance $(|Z|)$ with changes in applied potential. Typical results are shown in Fig. 11, and it is seen that the curves for apparent resistance and for $|Z|$ have similar shapes and, in particular, they both show a maximum for the optimum operating voltage. Some details of the role of hydration in the formation of anode films have been obtained from such studies of the variation of $|Z|$ for various solutions [4, 34].

The relation between cell resistance or impedance and cell voltage may be used in the development of polishing solutions. If a series

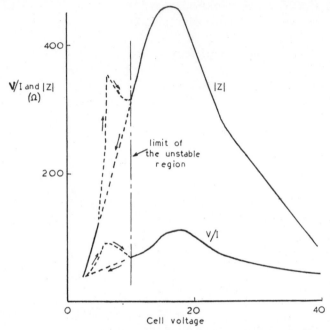

Fig. 11. Curves of cell resistance, V/I, and impedance, $|Z|$, as functions of cell voltage for a nickel anode in a perchloric acid-acetic anhydride solution [34]. $|Z|$ is measured at a frequency of 10 kc/s.

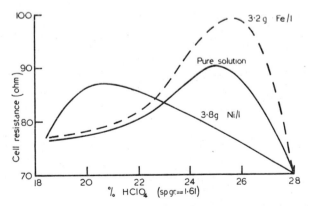

Fig. 12. Curves showing the variation of maximum cell resistance with composition, for perchloric acid solutions containing different amounts of dissolved metals [34, 35].

of solutions of different compositions is examined, the optimum polishing conditions for each can be determined by noting the maximum value of cell resistance or impedance. A plot of these values against composition gives a curve which shows a maximum at the optimum composition (Fig. 12). The composition thus found is characteristic of the metal, and the optimum composition for any single phase alloy can be calculated, using the weight proportions of the alloying metals [4, 34, 35].

2.3. RAPID DETERMINATION OF OPTIMUM OPERATING CONDITIONS

It is possible to predict a suitable polishing solution from chemical considerations (see § 1.3), but considerable research is often required to determine the optimum operating conditions.

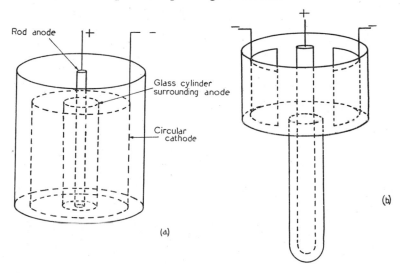

Fig. 13. Cells used by BERTEIN [36] for the study of polishing conditions over a range of anode current densities.

BERTEIN [36] discusses this problem, and proposes the use of electrolytic cells which allow simultaneous investigation of a large range of anode current densities. Two of his arrangements are shown in Figs. 13a, b. On applying a fixed current to these cells, the anodes show zones of varying surface finish, and inspection indicates whether the solution is suitable for polishing. If the solution is suitable, the optimum ranges of current density can be estimated roughly from the positions and lengths of the polished zones. The cell shown in Fig. 13b has the advantages of allowing observation of the anode during the passage of current and of accurate temperature control.

Quantitative information can be obtained from such cells by measurements of anode potential. LORKING [37] has approached the problem in this way, and developed a technique based on the Hull cell. His cell consists of two vertical electrodes placed at an angle so that the current density varies along the length of the anode. On applying a voltage across the cell, regions of varying surface finish are produced. LORKING measured the anode potentials corresponding to various surface finishes, and obtained good correlation with the results obtained using the curve of anode potential against anode current density. By varying the composition of the electrolyte, the optimum solution can be found readily, and the anode potential corresponding to the optimum polishing condition measured. The cell has been used to determine the optimum conditions for polishing copper in orthophosphoric acid solutions, and to investigate the effects of surface-active agents [38].

Such cells offer a simple means of investigating the optimum operating conditions of any metal/electrolyte combination. The effect of the size of the cell on these conditions is discussed in § 3.6.

CHAPTER 3

FACTORS INFLUENCING POLISHING CONDITIONS

3.1. POTENTIAL DIFFERENCE AND CURRENT DENSITY

THE electrical characteristics of the polishing process have been discussed in § 2, and only a few general features will be included here. In general, electropolishing in the laboratory is more satisfactory under conditions of controlled potential difference than under conditions of controlled current density, i.e. potentiometric circuits are more useful than series circuits. Apart from the difficulty of maintaining a constant current density, long periods of electrolysis at current densities much above the "natural"* value can result in gas evolution, which may cause pitting of the surface. Furthermore, during the initial stages of anodic attack before polishing conditions are established, a current density considerably higher than the natural value is desirable in order to minimize the time taken to establish polishing conditions. This high initial current density, as well as the natural current density for polishing, is achieved most simply by applying, from the beginning of electrolysis, a cell potential difference in the range of polishing.

However, when high current densities are necessary to produce polishing, the power loss is considerable for a potentiometric circuit (see Fig. 9), and in these cases a series circuit is used. In order that the series circuit should not be sensitive to changes in the resistance of the cell, it is necessary to have a large resistance in series with the cell, and hence a high voltage supply is required.

3.2. TEMPERATURE OF THE ELECTROLYTE

The resistance of an electrolyte decreases with increasing temperature, and thus the voltage required to give the same current density is less. The voltage, V, required to maintain a given current density is given by the empirical equation

$$V = K/(a\theta + b),$$

---

* The "natural" current density is the value observed when the cell voltage is maintained constant until a steady current density is achieved. This is the value used in curves of cell voltage against anode current density.

where θ is the temperature and K, a, and b are constants determined by the conductivity of the electrolyte, the dimensions of the cell, and the current passing through the cell [39]. It is clear from this equation that the power required to maintain a given current density decreases with increasing temperature. However, at high temperatures the viscosity of the bath decreases so that it is more difficult to maintain the viscous layer on the anode. Thus, an optimum temperature of operation should be chosen to minimize the power required without impairing the finish.

In some cases there is a considerable rise in the temperature of the solution during polishing, due partly to the resistance of the solution and partly to the presence of high resistance layers on the anode. The influence of high resistance layers on the anode is particularly noticeable with perchloric acid solutions where temperatures of 60 to 70°C have been measured on the anode while the bulk of the solution remains at about 20°C [40]. Such solutions are usually cooled by using a stainless steel container for the electrolyte and surrounding it with an ice-water bath. However, with larger volumes of solution, cooling coils through which water is circulated must be used. Care then has to be taken to ensure that the bath is not cooled below the critical point for precipitation of solid products on the anode; this is approximately 15 to 18°C for most perchloric acid solutions.

3.3. AGITATION OF THE ELECTROLYTE

During electrolysis under steady-state conditions, the reaction products tend to accumulate around the electrodes. In some cases, diffusion and convection cannot supply sufficient fresh electrolyte to the anode, and agitation is necessary to remove some of the reaction products and maintain the viscous layer at the optimum thickness for polishing. However, excessive agitation must be avoided as this can completely destroy the viscous layer and prevent the attainment of polishing conditions. Stirring or agitation also prevents excessive local heating due to the passage of current through the high resistance layers on the anode (see § 3.2), and maintains a more uniform temperature in the cell.

In many cases, the best results are obtained by rotating or oscillating the anode rather than by agitating the solution. In general, speeds of the order of 100 rev/min are suitable. However, it should be noted that a higher current density is required for a moving anode than for a stationary one, in order to maintain the viscous layer.

3.4. INITIAL PREPARATION OF SURFACE

In general the polishing time decreases with increasing fineness of initial finish. However, in some cases there appears to be an optimum roughness of initial finish, e.g. VON HAMOS [41] recommends that the initial finish be that given by mechanical polishing on 00 emery paper for copper, 400 emery paper for α-brass and aluminium, and 240 emery paper for white metal and steels. The uniform current density and lack of concentration gradients on a smooth surface appear to result in a relatively slow increase in metal ion concentration around the anode, and thus the establishment of polishing conditions may require a longer time with a smooth surface than with a rough surface. This is shown clearly by the different curves of cell voltage against anode current density which JACQUET [42] obtained for different initial finishes on steel specimens polished in a perchloric acid–acetic anhydride solution, using a series circuit. Similarly, a difference between mechanically polished and electropolished surfaces has been observed in the copper/orthophosphoric acid system, using a potentiometric circuit [29]. The shape of the curve of anode potential against anode current density remained unchanged for a range of initial abraded finishes, but when a previously electropolished surface was used, the peak on the curve corresponding to the appearance of the viscous layer was smaller, and the anode current density in the plateau region higher.

If the initial finish is too coarse, the time required to produce a smooth surface is long, and the amount of metal removed is excessive (see also § 4.4.1.)

3.5. TIME OF TREATMENT

The time of electrolysis necessary to produce a given polish naturally varies with the metal, the initial state of the surface, and the solution used. However, as an approximate general rule it has been found that the time of treatment necessary is inversely proportional to the current density used, i.e. the important quantity is the total amount of electricity passing through the solution. Thus solutions containing orthophosphoric acid, which operate at low current densities, require longer times than solutions containing perchloric acid, which operate at high current densities. In general, polishing times are of the order of minutes.

3.6. SIZE OF THE ELECTROPOLISHING SYSTEM

A very important factor in the operation of any electrochemical process is the size of the system, since changes in size can change the operating conditions considerably. This is partly the reason why solutions used in industrial electropolishing processes are different from those used for the same metal in the laboratory.

Consider two cells A and B that differ only in size [43]. For B to be a "true" model of A, i.e. for the current densities and the potentials in both cases to be the same at all corresponding points in the two cells, the ratio l/K (where l is the length of line joining two corresponding points on the electrodes in the cells and K is the specific conductivity) must be constant. Thus, K must be altered for any change in l.

CHAPTER 4

LABORATORY AND RESEARCH APPLICATIONS OF ELECTROLYTIC POLISHING

4.1. COMPARISON OF MECHANICALLY AND ELECTROLYTICALLY POLISHED SURFACES [44–46]

THE mechanical preparation of metallic surfaces for research or industrial purposes can be divided conveniently into two stages:

(a) "roughing down," using grinding and abrasion techniques to produce a reasonably smooth and macroscopically plane surface.

(b) "polishing," using fine abrasives on polishing pads to give a smooth and bright surface.

Considerable research has been carried out on the structure of metallic surfaces prepared by such methods, and it is now well established that mechanical preparation leads to a severely deformed zone near the surface. This zone has different properties to those of the bulk metal, and thus results obtained on mechanically polished surfaces are not characteristic of the bulk metal. Electron diffraction studies of mechanically polished surfaces show that the extreme surface layer is intensely deformed, and that the final smooth surface is produced by a flow process, i.e. the metal from the peaks is forced down into the hollows [47–49]. This surface layer is usually termed the "Beilby layer", and is considered to be approximately 50 Å thick*. The interpretation of electron diffraction patterns from such a thin layer is difficult, and opinion is divided as to whether the layer consists of amorphous metal or exceedingly fine crystals. The problem of the nature of the Beilby layer is largely a matter of terminology, since the size of the crystals, which must be assumed in order to explain the electron diffraction phenomena, is so small that the resulting structure is nearly amorphous. The stability of such amorphous material is difficult to explain, but recent research

---

* Recent work by SAMUELS and SANDERS [49] indicates that such a layer is present only on burnished surfaces and is not present on mechanically polished silver surfaces. Clearly further work is necessary to confirm this result.

[50] has shown that entrapped oxides can prevent grain growth in the intensely deformed surface zones. Thus, when very finely crystalline or apparently amorphous material is formed during polishing, it presumably remains stable due to the presence of entrapped oxides and polishing compound in the Beilby layer.

Between the Beilby layer and the undistorted bulk metal there is a relatively thick transition zone of deformed metal. The change

Table 4. Depth of Deformed Zone (micron) Produced by Representative Machining Processes [51]

Machining process	18/8 Stainless steel	Zinc
Lathe turned*	45	135
Machine surface ground†	35	125
Hand ground‡	43	130
Filing, 2nd cut §	46	130
Filing, smoothing §	34	70
Abrasion on linisher belt, 100 mesh §	12	85
Abrasion on Aloxite cloth, 150 mesh**	12	65

* Faced at high speed with 0·001 in. cuts; unlubricated.
† 0·005 in. cuts with a 60 grit wheel; lubricated with commercial cutting compound.
‡ Held lightly against a 60 grit side-faced wheel.
§ Unlubricated.
** Lubricated with paraffin.

in the degree of deformation with distance below the surface of an abraded specimen has been examined using X-ray and metallographic techniques [45, 51]. In the former method the thickness of the deformed zone is estimated by measuring the amount of metal that has to be removed by etching in order to obtain an X-ray pattern characteristic of undeformed metal.

In the latter method a taper section of the surface is made and the depth of the deformed zone is determined using etching techniques sensitive to small amounts of deformation (Figs. 14 and 15). Using this method, SAMUELS [51] has examined the deformation produced by various "roughing down" processes. Results for 18/8 stainless steel and zinc are given in Table 4; in the case of zinc, frictional heating of the extreme surface layers leads also to a recrystallized zone 20 to 30 microns thick (Fig. 14b).

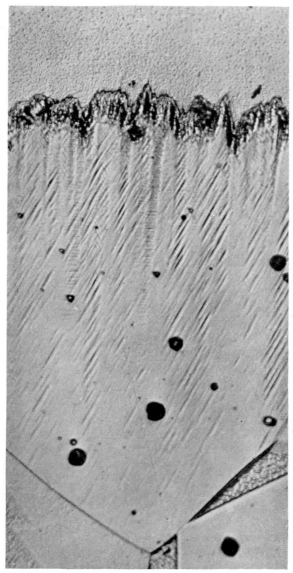

(*Courtesy of* L. E. Samuels)

Fig. 14a. Taper section of surface of 18/8 stainless steel after abrasion on 220-grade silicon carbide paper. Etched electrolytically in oxalic acid solution. Taper ratio 10 : 1 ($\times 1000$).

Fig. 14b. Taper section of surface of zinc after abrasion on 220-grade silicon carbide paper. Etched lightly in alcoholic phosphoric acid and examined under polarized light.
Taper ratio 13 : 6 : 1 (×250).

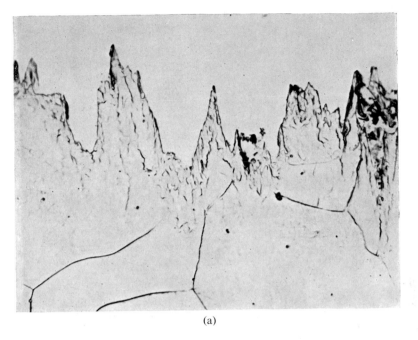

(a)

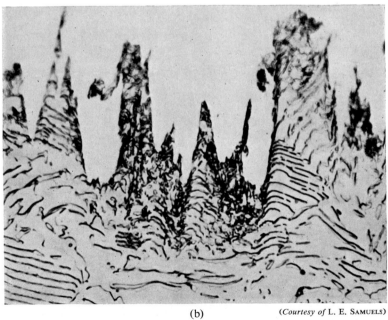

(b)   *(Courtesy of* L. E. Samuels)

Fig. 15. Taper sections of surfaces of (a) ingot iron and (b)
normalized 1 per cent carbon steel after abrasion on 220-grade
silicon carbide paper. Taper ratio 10 : 1 (×1500).

SAMUELS has also examined the deformation produced by metallographic abrasion processes normally used after the processes quoted in Table 4 and the results are given in Table 5.

Examples of such deformed zones produced in ferrite and pearlite by abrasion on 220-grade silicon carbide paper are shown in Fig. 15. In these cases the zones are very shallow and such defects should not appear in the final polished surface either after mechanical or

Table 5. Depth of Deformed Zone (microns) Produced by Various Metallographic Abrasion Processes [51]

Abrasive	Grade	18/8 Stainless steel	Zinc
Silicon carbide paper	220	6·0	45
	400	2·5	25
	600	2·2	15
Emery paper	1/0	5·0	40
	2/0	4·0	25
	3/0	4·0	24
	4/0	4·0	10–25*
Alumina-wax lap	(10–20) microns	1·5	15

* Depending on condition of the paper.

electrolytic polishing unless a very poor technique is used. However, as Tables 4 and 5 show, for other metals and alloys, the mere use of electrolytic polishing does not in itself ensure the production of surfaces free from deformation when the specimen has been subjected to preliminary abrasion treatments. Electrolytically polished surfaces can only be obtained completely free from deformation by continuing electrolysis for long enough to remove the entire deformed zone produced by initial mechanical preparation. If the rate of dissolution is known then the time necessary for production of a surface free from strain can be calculated. Dissolution rates for various metal/electrolyte combinations are listed in Appendix I. In the case of 18/8 stainless steel and zinc specimens finished on 600-grade silicon carbide paper, Appendix I indicates that electrolysis for 4 min and 75 min respectively is the minimum treatment needed to remove the deformed zones from these metals. The perfection of carefully electropolished surfaces is shown by the continuity of the structure of the bulk metal into electrodeposits on such surfaces [52].

It is interesting to note that the amount of metal removed during a typical mechanical preparation is approximately the same as that for a typical electrolytic preparation; figures for a steel specimen are given in Appendix II.

4.2. CHEMICAL NATURE OF ELECTROPOLISHED SURFACES [45]

When electrolytic polishing was first developed, it was believed that in all cases a smooth, brilliant, and active metal surface was produced, and that electrolytic polishing was the answer to all surface problems. However, it is now realized that, although electrolytic polishing offers a means of producing an undeformed surface, in some cases the surface is covered by a thin film of oxide or some other chemical compound. This is to be expected, since the formation of a film on the surface is an essential part of the polishing mechanism and, further, considerable oxidation can occur when the polished surface is exposed to moist air. Thus, although many studies have been made of the chemical nature of metal surfaces after electropolishing [44, 45, 53, 54], the results, even on the same metal, are often conflicting, due to the use of different solutions, washing techniques, and methods of examination.

The films present on surfaces after electropolishing are normally very thin, and do not influence greatly the etching characteristics of the metal. However, in those cases where thick films are present, some passivity may be conferred, so that long etching times are required. If the electropolished surface is used to study surface markings caused by plastic deformation, care must be taken to ensure that layers, either of chemical compounds or oxide, do not mask the true behaviour of the metal. For example, aluminium polished in fluoboric acid or orthophosphoric acid–ethyl alcohol solutions shows surface markings which are not characteristic of slip, but are due to the presence of a thick oxide layer which can be removed by careful etching [55, 56]. WILSDORF [57] has described a technique involving cathodic bombardment for removing such films from lead specimens. The resultant surface showed deformation markings which would have been obscured by the oxide film.

4.3. IMPERFECTIONS ON ELECTROPOLISHED SURFACES

Although an electropolished surface is generally smooth and brilliant, such ideal conditions are only obtained with pure metals or single phase alloys free from inclusions. Poor results are obtained with duplex and more complex alloys since local potential differences are set up which disturb the polishing equilibrium. For alloys, two cases can be distinguished:

(a) If the second phase is anodic to the matrix, the second phase is attacked preferentially and the intensity of the attack depends on the potential of the local cell between the second phase and the surrounding matrix. An example of this behaviour is the selective dissolution of silicon from aluminium–silicon alloys.

(b) If the second phase is cathodic to the matrix, the matrix is attacked preferentially around the particles of the second phase and these may become detached and leave pits in the surface. This may occur during the polishing of steels and cast irons.

In each case the effects are accentuated by increased current densities and longer polishing times. Even with pure metals and alloys free from inclusions, poor results may be obtained if the metal or alloy has been cold worked prior to electropolishing (see, for example, [58]).

Sometimes periodic structures are observed on electropolished surfaces and tend to mask the true structure of the metal. Such spurious structures may be observed if the initial surface is too rough, the time of polishing is too short or too long, the stirring is excessive or the optimum electrical conditions for polishing are not used.

Such structures on a microscopic scale have been discussed by VON HAMOS [41] and MERCHANT [59]. However, even under correct polishing conditions, a periodic structure on a submicroscopic scale (period of 1000 to 2000 Å for aluminium) has been observed on the surface [60]. Electron microscopy indicates that this periodic structure is not related to the substructure of the metal, but is a consequence of the electropolishing process since the character of the structure changes with variation in electrical conditions. This structure appears to be related to changes in the nature of the thin surface film (see § 1. 2. 4), and hence in the mode of dissolution of the metal. Clearly, however, care must be taken in the interpretation of apparent substructures observed during studies of electropolished surfaces with the electron microscope.

4.4. APPLICATIONS OF ELECTROLYTIC POLISHING*

4.4.1. Metallography

Electropolishing has been applied widely in metallography, its principal advantages being:

(a) *Simplicity*—Provided standard conditions of voltage, current density, temperature and composition of electrolyte are maintained, the process gives reproducible results. With mechanical polishing, the degree of finish obtained depends to a large extent on the skill of the operator.

(b) *Speed*—In general, the operation only requires 3 to 15 min. If a particularly rapid metallographic examination is necessary, special techniques are available for some metals for which the polishing time is only 30 sec.

(c) *Versatility*—On the one hand, extremely small areas can be polished using special techniques (see § 5.2), while on the other hand, large articles of complex shape can be polished by using auxiliary cathodes to obtain a uniform current density.

(d) *"Trueness" of surface*—Electropolishing can produce surfaces free from deformed zones. This is particularly important in the case of the soft metals such as lead and tin, and of stainless steels. All these metals are difficult to prepare for metallographic examination by mechanical polishing.

It should be noted that, apart from the commercial electropolishing units which operate at high densities, the use of diamond dust for metallographic polishing (see, for example [62]) has reduced greatly the advantage of the electrolytic polishing method for routine specimen preparation, since it is now possible to polish rapidly to a fine finish straight from a moderately coarse emery paper. In general, the long periods of polishing necessary for removing a thick deformed zone tend to produce a slightly wavy surface rather than a plane one. Therefore, if the surface of a specimen is required to be plane as well as free from a deformed zone, a useful technique is to polish with

---

* JACQUET [45, 61] gives fuller details and a bibliography on this subject.

diamond dust to a fine finish and then electropolish for a much shorter time than usual (about a quarter the usual time) to remove any deformed zone present.

In most cases, the differential attack associated with the electro-polishing of multiphase alloys (see § 4.3) is a disadvantage and care must be taken in interpreting the resultant structure. However, it can be used as a sensitive method for differential etching of traces of an insoluble constituent [63] or of precipitated phases [64]. A rapid and readily controlled etching procedure is the "short circuit" technique used by JACQUET [65] for copper and its alloys. This consists of shorting the electrodes together immediately the polishing current is switched off. The small potential generated by the difference between the concentrations around the electrodes leads to etching of the anode.

4.4.2. Preparation of surfaces for research

From the discussion of § 4.1 it is clear that, in general, physical and chemical properties which have been determined on mechanically polished surfaces are not characteristic of the bulk metal. However, if the necessary precautions are taken, electropolishing methods can produce a brilliant, smooth, film-free surface with properties characteristic of the metal rather than of the method of preparation. Thus, electropolishing has been used very extensively for surface preparation prior to oxidation and corrosion measurements [66], measurement of optical constants [67], measurement of friction and surface damage at light loads [68], measurement of microhardness values [69] and studies of deformation of metals [70,71].

4.4.3. Specialized applications

One of the main features of electropolishing is that the rate of dissolution can be controlled accurately and this had led to the use of the process for production of fine wire and strip [4, 72–74]. A schematic apparatus for the continuous production of fine wire is shown in Fig. 16. In the case of stainless steel, by starting with wire 0·0004 to 0·001 in. thick, a final diameter of 0·00015 in. can be obtained consistently [74]. Thin strip produced in this fashion may have different magnetic and electrical characteristics from strip of larger size. EPELBOIN [4] has found that if cold worked material is used, the final resistivity depends markedly on the initial thickness and the amount of metal removed. This variation is due to the

Table 6. Solutions Suitable for the Preparation of Very Thin Foils for Transmission Electron Microscopy (after TOMLINSON [75])

Metal	Composition	Cathode	Voltage across cell	Current (A)	Temp. (°C)	Remarks
Stainless steel	60 ml orthophosphoric acid 40 ml sulphuric acid	Stainless steel	9	3	60	Technique due to BOLLMANN [75] used in both cases.
Silicon steel	As above	As above	20, falling to 9	7	Below 60	
Magnesium	33 ml nitric acid 67 ml methyl alcohol	Stainless steel	9	1	Below 30	Technique described by TOMLINSON [75] used in all these cases.
Copper α-brass	As above As above	Copper Copper	4–8 7–8	1 1·2	As above As above	
Cobalt	23 ml perchloric acid 77 ml glacial acetic acid	Stainless steel	22	1·5	As above	
Nickel	As above	As above	20–30	1·5	As above	
Aluminium	20 ml perchloric acid 80 ml ethyl alcohol	Aluminium	19–20	0·4	As above	
Iron	5 ml perchloric acid 95 ml glacial acetic acid	Stainless steel	35–45	1·5	As above	

inhomogeneous deformation produced by the fabrication process. Annealing prior to electropolishing reduces the variation in final resistivity.

A recent application of increasing importance is the preparation of very thin specimens for transmission electron microscopy by controlled electropolishing [75]. Two techniques have been employed. The first, due to BOLLMANN [75], employs pointed cathodes held close to each side of the sheet or foil anode; localized solution occurs leaving a thinned region supported by metal of approximately the

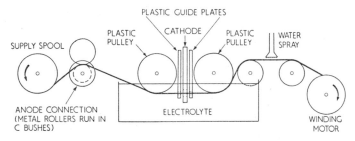

Fig. 16. Schematic diagram of an apparatus for the production of fine wire by electropolishing [72].

initial thickness. This technique appears to be particularly suited to ferrous materials. The second technique, described by TOMLINSON [75], is to coat the sheet or foil with polystyrene leaving only a small square "window" (approximately $\frac{1}{2}$ in. by $\frac{1}{2}$ in.) on either side of the foil. By using plane cathodes close to the anode, the foil of the window can be thinned down to the required thickness. This is usually not a uniform process but a suitable section can be removed readily for examination. By switching the current on and off rapidly during the last few seconds of treatment, specimens can be produced which are uniformly thin over reasonable areas.

The time of treatment can vary from 30 sec to 10 min depending on the initial thickness (usually 0·001 to 0·01 in.) and the current density used. Since solutions which are used for electropolishing bulk material are not always suitable for thinning, a list of solutions for thinning various metals and alloys is given in Table 6.

The technique of "jet etching", in which a jet of electrolyte is used to produce a localized thin section on transistors [76], also appears to be suitable for the preparation of very thin specimens for transmission electron microscopy from bulk material.

4

CHAPTER 5

GENERAL PRINCIPLES
FOR LABORATORY METHODS

5.1. REQUIREMENTS OF A CELL FOR ELECTROPOLISHING

THE principal requirements of an electropolishing cell are as follows:

(1) The anode connection should be constructed so that the specimen may be removed from the cell easily and quickly for washing and subsequent treatment. It should be made of corrosion-resistant material, or else covered with some inert film so that only the specimen is exposed to the solution.

(2) The specimen should only be in contact with the electrolyte when the required potential difference for polishing exists. Thus, the current must be switched on before the specimen is immersed in the electrolyte and the specimen should be removed and washed quickly before the current is switched off.

(3) Only the portion of the specimen to be polished should be in contact with the electrolyte. This can be achieved in several ways:

(a) by covering the rest of the specimen with some inert film, e.g. paraffin wax or lacquer;

(b) by immersing only the face to be polished, either by placing it just below the solution level or by clamping it against a hole in the wall of the cell; or

(c) by mounting the specimen in plastic. Electrical contact is made by drilling a hole through the mount and inserting a covered contact lead. A drop of mercury ensures good electrical contact at the junction between the lead and the specimen.

(4) The position of the specimen, with respect to the cathode, should remain fixed during electrolysis, so that no unnecessary variation of the internal resistance of the cell occurs. In most of the cases where polishing occurs under viscous layer conditions, the anode is placed horizontally to maintain a stable layer, while in most of the cases where polishing occurs with gas evolution, the anode is placed vertically to allow easy escape of the gas bubbles.

If a specimen which is usually polished in a horizontal position is treated in a vertical position, a higher current density is necessary to maintain polishing conditions since the viscous layer tends to stream off the surface, e.g. copper in orthophosphoric acid requires a current density of 6 A/dm^2 in the horizontal position and 9 A/dm^2 in vertical position. The finish obtained in such cases is generally poorer in the vertical position.

(5) The cathode should be placed so that the gas evolved will not destroy the viscous layer at the anode. During electropolishing, metal is deposited on the cathode in a very loosely adherent form, since the conditions are unfavourable for electroplating. Thus, the cathode should be as large as possible so that this deposit is distributed sparsely over its surface and the danger of discrete particles leaving the cathode and interfering with the polishing process is reduced to a minimum. A large cathode also tends to even out the current distribution on the anode.

(6) The cell should permit some agitation of the electrolyte either by stirring or by rotation of the anode and/or cathode during polishing.

(7) The temperature of the electrolyte should be kept constant during electrolysis.

(8) The cathode should not react with the electrolyte.

5.2. APPARATUS SUITABLE FOR ELECTROPOLISHING IN THE LABORATORY

The electrical characteristics of the polishing process have been discussed in § 2 and it was noted there that for solutions where a large potential drop occurs across the cell, a series circuit should be used, while a potentiometric circuit is more suitable for solutions where a small potential drop occurs across the cell. The general layout of these two circuits is illustrated in Fig. 17. Two different electrode arrangements are shown and the set-up to be used depends on the position of the specimen, as discussed in § 5.1.

For low voltages a battery supply is normally used. However, for high voltages a battery bank would be necessary and it is therefore more convenient to use a rectifier. If the ripple of the rectified wave form is small it has little or no effect on the process. Larger ripples would be expected to have some effect, but steel and nickel have been polished with 50 and 60 c/s a.c. [77], the results being similar

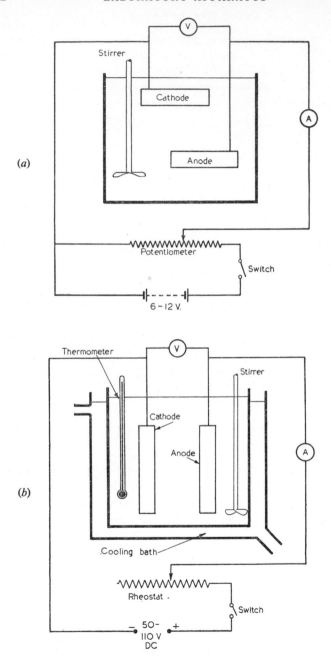

Fig. 17. Circuits used for electropolishing in the laboratory:
(a) Potentiometric circuit, for low current densities;
(b) Series circuit, for high current densities.

to those produced by d.c. It appears that under these conditions of operation the normal mechanism of polishing operates during the positive portion of the cycle.

A simple circuit which gives a wide range of voltages from a rectified source has been described by Pow [78] and is shown in Fig. 18. The circuit consists of a 250 V 50 c/s a.c. source connected

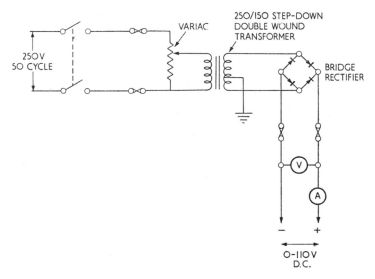

Fig. 18. Rectifier circuit used by Pow [78] to provide a suitable range of voltages for polishing.

through a fuse switch to a Variac transformer which is connected to a 250/150 V step-down double-wound transformer. The output from the transformer is rectified by a bridge rectifier rated at 10 A continuously, but which may be used for short periods up to 15 A. By means of the Variac the d.c. output from the rectifier may be varied volt by volt from zero to approximately 110 V (at full load).

A similar circuit which includes a bridge circuit for controlling the polishing conditions by using the maximum on the curve of cell resistance against cell voltage (see § 2.2) has been given by HANCHER [79]. The circuit is shown in Fig. 19 and for operation the variable resistor is adjusted to approximately the resistance of the cell circuit, the voltage from the transformer is gradually

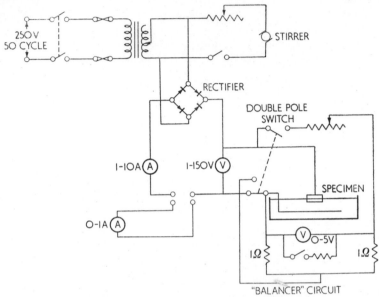

Fig. 19. Circuit used by HANCHER [79] for polishing under optimum conditions.

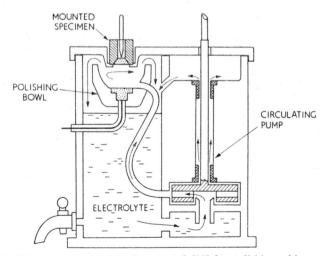

Fig. 20. Apparatus used by SYKES *et al.* [80] for polishing with a constant flow of electrolyte across the surface of the anode.

increased and the resistance changes read on the bridge voltmeter. The maximum resistance is noted and the settings adjusted to keep the circuit in balance at this value. The balancing operation should be carried out as quickly as possible, since heating of the electrolyte in the cell reduces the resistance and thus masks the maximum value.

In most cases agitation of the electrolyte is carried out either by a simple stirrer or by rotating the anode. However, in some cases it is desirable to maintain a smooth constant flow of electrolyte across the surface of the anode. SYKES *et al.* [80] have described an apparatus for this purpose (Fig. 20); it has been designed specifically for polishing uranium but should be suitable for other metals. The whole apparatus is constructed from polyethylene plastic ("Alkathene" or "polythene") which is inert to most acids and alkalies and is relatively easy to machine.

The principles outlined above have been incorporated in commercial electropolishing units using rectified d.c. and several types have been described in the technical literature.* Some of these units use an external cell from which the electrodes may be removed readily and in which agitation is effected either by a stirrer or by rotation of the electrodes. However, a controlled flow system in which electrolyte is pumped across a selected area of the specimen surface appears to be more suitable for routine use. The original unit using this sytem was the "Disa-Electropol" [86] (illustrated in Fig. 21) which is used extensively for routine preparation of many metals and alloys, for example, aluminium and light alloys [88] and zirconium, titanium and beryllium [99]. An example of a more

* These commercial electropolishing units are:

U.K.   —(1) Electropolishing equipment made by Nash & Thompson Ltd., Surrey [81].

        (2) "The Shandon Electropolisher" made by Shandon Scientific Co. Ltd., London [85].

U.S.A.   —(1) The "Buehler-Waisman" electropolisher made by Buehler Ltd., Chicago [82].

        (2) The "Cenco-Hangosky" electropolisher made by Central Scientific Co., Chicago [83].

        (3) The "Precision Electrolytic Polisher" made by Fisher Scientific Co., Pittsburgh—St. Louis—Montreal [84].

Denmark—(1) The "Disa-Electropol" and the "Micropol" made by Struers Chemiske Laboratorium, Copenhagen, Denmark [86].

recent unit using this system is the "Shandon Electropolisher" (Fig. 22) which is a modified design of the apparatus shown in Fig. 20. In this unit, the electrolyte is pumped through a series of orifices so that it contacts the specimen in the form of a rotating and continuously renewed vertical column of liquid. Such a system prevents the formation of flow lines on the specimen, particularly in multiphase alloys showing marked relief effects between the phases [85].

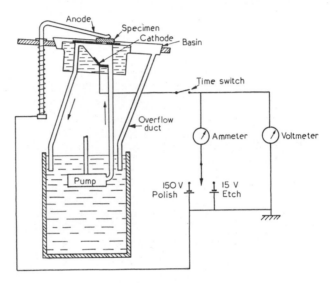

Fig. 21. Diagrammatic sketch of "Disa-Electropol" unit [86, 88].

All of these commercial units polish only a small area and are so designed that a sample must be taken from the metal object being examined. In many cases it is impossible to cut such a sample, and examination *in situ* is necessary. Various electropolishing devices have been developed for this purpose. The "Micropol" [86] uses a pipette type of cell (Fig. 23) and only a small area (about 1 mm^2) is polished. A slightly larger area (about 0·5 cm^2) can be polished using the "Movipol" [87] which is a small portable cell using a flow system and designed for use with the "Disa-Electropol."

Another variation of the conventional apparatus is the technique of "brush polishing" [89]. Here the anode rests against a layer of glass wool covering the cathode and the electrolyte is forced through perforations in the cathode so that the glass wool is kept soaked

Fig. 22. Photograph of the polishing unit of the "Shandon Electropolisher" showing pump, electrolytic cell containing specially
shaped stainless steel cathode and specimen clamp. The unit is
connected to a separate power supply.

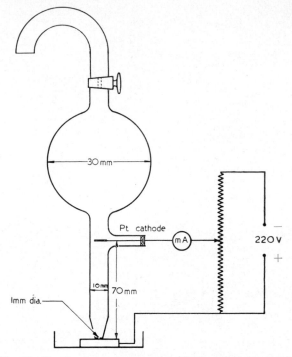

Fig. 23. Sketch of apparatus used for "Micro-Polishing" [86].

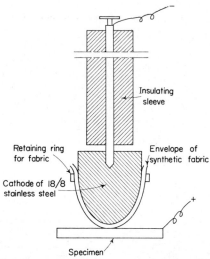

Fig. 24. Sketch of tampon for "Ellopol" [90].

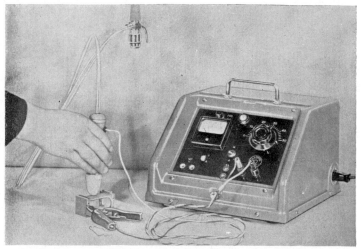

(*Courtesy of* Société d'Applications de Procédés Électrolytiques)

Fig. 25. Photograph of "Ellopol" showing power supply, tampon with provision for water cooling and clamp for anode connection to specimen.

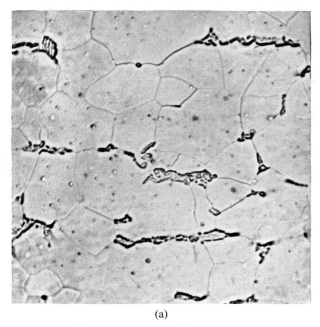

(a)

Fig. 26. (See next page for caption.)

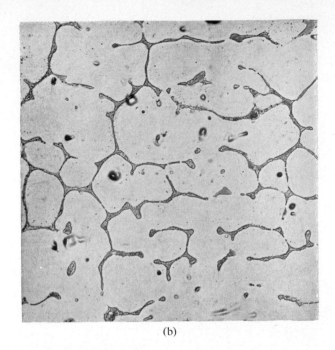

(b)

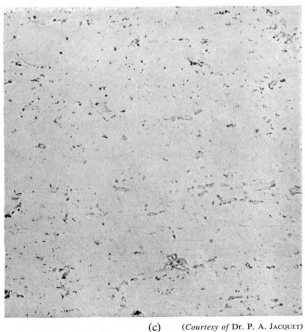

(c)   *(Courtesy of* Dr. P. A. JACQUET)

Fig. 26. Examples of specimens prepared with "Ellopol":
(a) Section of mild steel sheet, 2 mm thick ($\times 400$);
(b) Aluminium—8 per cent copper—1 per cent manganese alloy, as
    cast ($\times 160$);
(c) Strip of copper—2 per cent beryllium alloy, 0·26 mm thick
    ($\times 400$).

with electrolyte. The polishing conditions differ from those normally used in that a much higher current density is obtained on the anode for similar applied voltages. Recently, this technique has been developed further by JACQUET [90] who uses a massive metallic electrode ("tampon") surrounded by sheets of synthetic fibres which are sufficient to retain an appreciable quantity of electrolyte. A typical form of the tampon is shown in Fig. 24 and a commercial apparatus on this principle, the "Ellopol",* in Fig. 25. The specimen can be polished either by rubbing the tampon over the surface or by using successive touches in cases where there is a marked temperature rise at the fibre/specimen interface as, for example, with perchloric acid solutions.

Not all conventional electrolytes can be used successfully for "tampon polishing", but JACQUET [90] has developed electrolytes for a wide range of metals and alloys. Compositions of recommended electrolytes are given in Table 7, and the conditions for polishing various metals and alloys in Table 8. The time of polishing depends on the initial condition of the surface and the size of the area to be polished, but is usually of the order of 30 to 60 sec with perchloric acid and nitric acid electrolytes, and several minutes with ortho-phosphoric acid electrolytes. Typical rates of anodic dissolution for various metal/solution combinations are given in Table 9.

Although originally developed for use on large sections the tampon method can also be used for metallographic preparation in the laboratory (see examples in [90]), and is particularly useful for the examination of thin sheets and tubes (Fig. 26). The method has been used also for electrolytic etching of stainless steels and nickel alloys, and for anodic oxidation of light alloys. The range of the technique can be extended considerably by use of special plastic replicas developed by VAN EFFENTERRE (see [90]). These replicas enable the structure of large objects to be examined in the laboratory, the surface changes during fatigue of parts in service to be followed, and the structure of highly radioactive specimens to be examined without special precautions.

* The "Ellopol", the special electrolytes and the replica technique ("Replic") discussed later are marketed exclusively by:

    Société d'Applications de Procédés Électrolytiques,
      126, Av. Pierre Brossolette, Malakoff (Seine), Paris.

Table 7. Compositions of Electrolytes for Tampon Polishing [90]

Electrolyte type	Active acid	Concentration (g/100 ml of solution)	Solvent
A	Orthophosphoric	34	Ethanol
B	Nitric	28	Methanol
C-1		5·7	Glacial
C-2	Perchloric	10	acetic
C-3		23·7	acid
C-4		26·6	
D	Perchloric	16	Methanol

Table 8. Conditions for Tampon Polishing [90]

Metal	Electrolyte	Voltage
Copper and copper alloys	A	10–15
	B	15–20
Iron, carbon steels, austenitic manganese steels	C-2	30–40
Nickel–chromium ferritic and	C-2	
austenitic stainless steels	C-3	20–30
Aluminium and light alloys	D	20–30
Magnesium and its alloys	D	15–20
Nickel, cobalt and their alloys	C-2	25–30
Chromium	C-1	30
	D	20–25
Titanium and certain of its alloys	C-2	40–50
Uranium, zirconium and their alloys	C-4	20–25
	D	20–25

Table 9. *Typical Rates of Anodic Dissolution
During Tampon Polishing* [90]

Metal	Solution	Approximate rate (micron per min)
Copper and its alloys {	A	2
	B	15
Carbon steels	C-2	4
Light alloys	D	10–12

CHAPTER 6

THE USE OF PERCHLORIC ACID
AND OTHER REACTIVE SOLUTIONS
IN ELECTROPOLISHING*

6.1. INTRODUCTION

PERCHLORIC acid has been used extensively as a constituent of
electropolishing solutions because of its unique properties, particularly its easy solution in non-aqueous solvents, its powerful
dissolving action on metals and alloys and the appreciable solubility
of many of the metallic perchlorates in acid media. For many
metals and alloys perchloric acid solutions give a more highly
polished and less oxidized surface than any of the other solutions
proposed. However, there have been several reports in the technical
literature of explosions caused by perchloric acid solutions† and
considerable research has been carried out to determine the influence
of the composition of such solutions on their explosive properties.
The results of this research will be discussed in some detail.

6.2. EXPLOSIVE PROPERTIES OF SOLUTIONS
USED IN PRACTICE

Perchloric acid polishing solutions can be divided into two main
classes, as will be seen from Table 10.

(a) Strong solutions, containing perchloric acid mixed with acetic
anhydride or acetic acid. These usually contain 1 part of
hydrated perchloric acid to about 2 parts of acetic anhydride
(or an equivalent amount of acetic acid).

(b) Less concentrated solutions containing perchloric acid mixed
with ethyl alcohol, acetic acid or acetic anhydride. These
solutions usually contain 1 part of hydrated perchloric acid
to about 4 parts of ethyl alcohol or similar amounts of acetic
acid or acetic anhydride. Sometimes 3 per cent of ether is
added. When mixing such electrolytes containing alcohol,

---

* This discussion is based on that of KEMSLEY and TEGART [91].
† JACQUET [92] gives a full discussion of all the recorded cases.

50

Table 10. Compositions of Perchloric Acid Electrolytes

Solution No.	Metal	Perchloric acid (ml)	Acetic anhydride (ml)	Acetic acid (ml)	Water (ml)	Ethyl alcohol (ml)	References
		(a) *Strong solutions*					
1	Aluminium	345 (sp. gr. 1·55)	655				JACQUET [93]
2	Cadmium	200 (sp. gr. 1·60)	800				HONEYCOMBE [94]
3	Lead	350 (sp. gr. 1·61)	630		20		JACQUET [95]
4	Magnesium	300 (sp. gr. 1·60)	700				BLACK [96]
5	Nickel	210 (sp. gr. 1·61)	790				JACQUET and FIGOUR [97]
6	Steels, Titanium	185 (sp. gr. 1·61)	765		50		JACQUET and ROCQUET [98], JACQUET [99]
7	Tin	100 (sp. gr. 1·60)					PUTTICK [100]
		(b) *Less concentrated*					
8	Aluminium, Lead, Tin and Zinc	54 (sp. gr. 1·68)			146	800	DE SY and HAEMERS [10]
9	Steels, Chromium, Titanium, Zirconium and Uranium	50 (sp. gr. 1·60)		1000	5–15		JACQUET [99, 101], JACQUET and CAILLAT [102]
10	Tin	63 (sp. gr. 1·48)		300	12		PERRYMAN [103]

esters may be formed. Their concentration would be low in these solutions but the danger of explosion would increase if the solutions became concentrated. Some workers consider that ethyl perchlorate, for example, is as dangerous as nitroglycerine.

The explosive and combustible properties of perchloric acid solutions can be represented conveniently on the triangular diagram of Fig. 27 [104]. Mixtures containing less than 55 wt. per cent

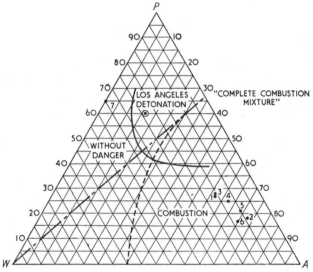

Fig. 27. Diagram illustrating the properties of mixtures of perchloric acid, acetic anhydride and water [104, 105]. The compositions are expressed in wt. per cent and the numbered compositions correspond to the solutions listed in Table 5.

perchloric acid cannot be detonated; these lie in the triangular region below the line joining A to the point on the PW axis corresponding to 55 wt. per cent perchloric acid (sp. gr. 1·48). The region to the right of the dotted line in the figure includes compositions which are liable to be inflamed by sparks or general heating. Once combustion begins in these mixtures, it tends to increase in speed and the burning of a large volume of liquid can develop into an explosion. The compositions of mixtures which are theoretically "safe", from the viewpoints of combustion and explosion, are therefore those in the lower left-hand portion of the diagram.

However, for optimum polishing conditions, higher acetic anhydride contents are necessary. The choice of composition is governed by the electrical conductivity of the solution and its ability to form a viscous layer on the anode. Unfortunately, suitable polishing mixtures lie in the inflammable range. The compositions of solutions 1 to 7 in Table 10(a) have been represented by points 1 to 7 on Fig. 27. These solutions may be used without any danger of explosion by detonation, but are liable to be inflamed by sparks, possibly leading to an explosion. If the precautions listed below are observed, little danger of explosion or combustion exists in the use of acetic anhydride–perchloric acid mixtures. The most damaging explosion reported was at Los Angeles, and the composition of the solution used lay well within the range of explosive mixtures (cf. Fig. 27).

6.3. PRECAUTIONS TO BE TAKEN WHEN USING PERCHLORIC ACID SOLUTIONS

The following general rules should always be observed when using perchloric acid solutions.

(1) Rubber protective equipment should be used in handling the mixtures, and such equipment should be cleaned promptly when it has become contaminated with the acid. Perchloric acid is a strong acid and is very corrosive to the skin.

(2) Perchloric acid should be stored away from all inflammable materials. It is preferable that containers be surrounded by enough inert inorganic packing material, e.g. Kieselguhr, to absorb the acid in case a container should break. If such precautions are not taken, breakage may result in the acid reacting with organic materials, such as wood, to produce a potentially explosive mixture. This hazard becomes clear from the statement of ELLIOT and BROWN [105] that mixtures of 60 per cent perchloric acid and wood meal had a greater explosive power than TNT when tested in a ballistic mortar.

(3) Perchloric acid solutions should not be used to polish alloys containing bismuth, as an explosive compound may form in this case.

(4) Perchloric acid solutions should not be used in contact with organic materials, since, if local heating occurs, the danger of a violent explosion is increased. This danger is even greater if iron is present in the solution.

(5) "Bakelite" or "Lucite" mounting materials, and cellulose-base insulating lacquers and materials should not be used in perchloric acid solutions. However, polyethylene ("Alkathene" or "polythene") and polystyrene plastics, ebonite and polyvinyl chloride synthetic rubber can be used without danger.

(6) Care should be taken to keep the temperature of the liquid below 35 to 40°C during mixing of perchloric acid and acetic anhydride (or ethyl alcohol), since much heat is evolved. Previously the recommended procedure was to add acetic anhydride to perchloric acid, but MEDARD, JACQUET and SARTORIUS [104] now recommend the reverse procedure, i.e. the slow addition of perchloric acid to acetic anhydride. Referring to Fig. 27 it will be seen that this procedure avoids the passage of the composition through the explosive range. During preparation, the mixture sometimes acquires a violet coloration, but this is not a danger sign. It is characteristic of the presence of minute amounts of Mn^{VII} ion which probably arises from the catalyst used in the production of the anhydride. This coloration is not lasting and changes to a brown tint, the intensity of which depends on the maximum temperature reached during mixing. The mixture should be thoroughly stirred during preparation since the densities of perchloric acid and acetic anhydride differ widely.

(7) Electrolysis of perchloric acid solutions is accompanied by rapid heating of that portion of the electrolyte in contact with the anode. Cooling and stirring arrangements may be necessary to maintain the temperature of the solution below 35°C to avoid possible combustion or explosion. The electrodes should be placed so that localized heating above 35°C cannot occur either during polishing or during removal of the article for washing.

(8) Provision should be made for adequate ventilation wherever perchloric acid–acetic anhydride mixtures are used, since the acetic anhydride gives off obnoxious fumes, particularly when heated.

(9) The distillation of discarded polishing solutions to recover the alcohol should not be attempted.

6.4. OTHER REACTIVE SOLUTIONS

Some electropolishing solutions consist of a strong oxidizing agent, e.g. nitric acid or chromic acid, mixed with an organic chemical, e.g. acetic anhydride or methyl alcohol, which can be oxidized. The exothermic oxidation reaction, if allowed to accelerate, can proceed sufficiently violently to cause a mild explosion which may cause injury to the operator because of the corrosive nature of the reactants [106]. Such a reaction may occur after an induction period of a few minutes. Initial heating which will cause the acceleration of the reaction may occur either by slow oxidation or by hydration of one of the constituents, e.g. acetic anhydride or sulphuric acid.

The following general rules should always be observed when using such solutions.

(1) Rubber protective equipment should be used in handling the mixtures and the mixing operation carried out behind a screen.

(2) Care must be taken that these solutions are not overheated during use and especially during mixing when it is essential that the reagents be kept cool and mixed very slowly.

(3) In most cases the oxidizing substance (plus any inert substances in the solution) should be added slowly to the reducing substance so that the concentration of the oxidizing substance is never greater than in the final solution. However, in several cases, the reverse procedure is recommended as indicated in the tables.

(4) Ethyl alcohol should not be used instead of methyl alcohol in solutions based on nitric acid since solutions of the former with nitric acid are very unstable and tend to decompose violently.

(5) Provision should be made for adequate ventilation whenever mixtures containing acetic anhydride are used, since the acetic anhydride gives off obnoxious fumes especially when heated.

(6) Care should be taken when mixing solutions containing sulphuric acid and water because of the large heat of hydration of the acid.

CHAPTER 7

LABORATORY METHODS FOR SPECIFIC METALS AND THEIR ALLOYS

METHODS are now available for electropolishing all the common metals and their alloys and several of the rarer metals and their alloys. The solutions listed in the following tables have been selected critically from the literature and in many cases have been tested in the Division of Tribophysics.

In most cases the solutions given for a particular metal will produce a satisfactory polish on its single phase alloys. When the alloys are duplex, the polish may not be satisfactory due to differential attack of the two phases (see § 4.3). In such cases, some modification of the solution or of the operating conditions may be necessary.

For certain alloys used either commercially, e.g. Nichrome and Nimonic, or in research, e.g. manganese–copper alloys, specific electrolytes have been developed and these have been listed in Table 25.

In general, different electrolytes are required for different metals, but there are some electrolytes which are capable of polishing several metals and these are useful in laboratories where a variety of metals is polished for routine examination. These electrolytes are listed in Table 26 together with the metals for which they have been used. Usually such solutions are not satisfactory for research purposes.

Except where otherwise stated, the acids in the solutions are concentrated reagent grade acids of the following specific gravities:

orthophosphoric acid	(98 per cent)	sp. gr. 1·84
sulphuric acid	(98·08 per cent)	sp. gr. 1·84
nitric acid	(63·02 per cent)	sp. gr. 1·40
hydrochloric acid	(36·47 per cent)	sp. gr. 1·175
glacial acetic acid	(60·05 per cent)	sp. gr. 1·065

Table 11. Aluminium

Composition	Cathode	Voltage	C.D. (A/dm²)	Time	Temp. (°C)	Circuit	Ref. No.	Remarks
345 ml perchloric acid (sp. gr. 1·55) 655 ml acetic anhydride	Aluminium	50–70* 22–30†	0·8–2·5	30–60 min (research) or 7–10 min (routine)	Below 35	Pot.	93, 107, 108	Useful where a smooth, strain-free surface is required. During polishing the anode should be agitated slowly in the solution; agitation of the solution only produces "grooving" on the anode. The anodic film should be removed by washing with a strong jet of cold water. To increase the viscosity and enhance polishing, 5 g/l aluminium should be added to solution before use. Solution should be handled with care (see § 6). Detailed conditions for different alloys are given in ref. 107, Part III, Chapters I, II, VI.
50 ml perchloric acid (sp. gr. 1·60) 1000 ml glacial acetic acid	Aluminium or stainless steel	50–55* 25–30†	10–15	10–25 sec	Below 35	Series	101	Useful for rapid specimen preparation. During polishing, the anode should be agitated in the solution, preferably by rotation. Prolonged polishing time causes the solution to heat up and produces etching of the anode. This electrolyte is non-explosive but care should be taken when handling perchloric acid (see § 6).
200 ml perchloric acid (sp. gr. 1·25) 800 ml ethyl alcohol	Stainless steel	110–220* 35–70†	100–400	10–25 sec	Below 35	Series	10, 109	Useful for rapid specimen preparation. The high current densities used lead to a "polish attack" of the anode. Most aluminium alloys, except those containing Si or Mg_2Si, can be polished satisfactorily for routine examination. Detailed operating conditions for different alloys are given in ref. 107, Part III, Chap. III, IV and V. Solution should be handled with care (see § 6).

* Voltage applied to circuit
† Approximate voltage drop across cell

Table 11 (cont.) Aluminium

Composition	Cathode	Voltage	C.D. (A/dm²)	Time	Temp. (°C)	Circuit	Ref. No.	Remarks
70 ml perchloric acid (sp. gr. 1·61) 1680 ml methyl alcohol 250 ml glycerine	Aluminium	110* 70–80†	50–150	10–20 sec	Below 35	Series	107	Used for polishing Al-Si alloys. Precautions must be taken against sparking and over-heating, since the solution is inflammable.
200 ml perchloric acid (sp. gr. 1·48) 1000 ml ethyl alcohol	Carbon or aluminium	50–60* 20†	30	2 min	Below 35	Pot.	103	Modification of "polish attack" method already given. Larger areas can be polished due to smaller currents passing. Care must be taken when handling this solution (see § 6).
400 ml ortho-phosphoric acid 380 ml ethyl alcohol 250 ml distilled water	Aluminium	50–60* 22–30†	35	4–6 min	42–45	Series	110	Anode rotation is necessary, with a small anode to cathode distance. With continued use, aluminium phosphate is deposited in the cell. This buffers the solution and changes its internal resistance, permitting polishing over a greater temperature range with same c.d. but with 35 V.† The anodic film should be removed by washing with a strong jet of cold water.
820 ml ortho-phosphoric acid 135 ml sulphuric acid 160 g chromium trioxide 100 ml water	Aluminium	60* 10†	12	5 min	95	Series	111	Solution is stable in operation. The temperature is fairly critical; if it falls below 95°C oxidation occurs.

* Voltage applied to circuit
† Approximate voltage drop across cell

Table 12. *Beryllium and Bismuth*

Metal	Composition	Cathode	Voltage	C.D. (A/dm²)	Time	Temp. (°C)	Circuit	Ref. No.	Remarks
Beryllium	100 ml perchloric acid (sp. gr. 1·20) 350 ml ethyl alcohol 100 ml butyl cellosolve	Stainless steel	50*	75–90	30–45 sec	Below 35	Series	99	Specimen should be moved rapidly through the solution above a horizontal cathode. Solution has also been used in the "Disa-Electropol" (see § 5.2) with 40 V for 20 to 25 sec.
Beryllium	100 ml orthophosphoric acid 30 ml sulphuric acid 30 ml glycerol 30 ml ethyl alcohol	Stainless steel		200–400		20	Series	112	Good metallographic polish without grain delineation. Surface has marked reaction to polarized light.
Bismuth	980 ml saturated potassium iodide solution 20 ml hydrochloric acid	Stainless steel or carbon	5–7†	20	Periods of 30 sec	20	Pot.	23, 113	Polish in periods of 30 sec allowing brown film formed to dissolve in solution between periods. Good reaction to polarized light.

* Voltage applied to circuit
† Approximate voltage drop across cell

Table 13. Cadmium, Chromium and Cobalt

Metal	Composition	Cathode	Voltage	C.D. (A/dm^2)	Time	Temp. (°C)	Circuit	Ref. No.	Remarks
Cadmium	200 ml perchloric acid (sp. gr. 1·60) 800 ml acetic anhydride	Cadmium	50-60* 25-35†	60-100	1 min or more	Below 35	Series	94	When solution is new and contains little dissolved metal, the temperature required for good polishing is somewhat higher than that for an older solution. Time may be longer than 1 min if a deformed surface zone is to be removed. Care must be taken when handling this solution (see § 6).
Cadmium	200 ml orthophosphoric acid 200 ml glycerol 100 ml distilled water	Cadmium	8-9†	40	5-10 min	20	Series	112	Slight etching but good reaction of surface to polarized light. "Polish-attack" method.
Cadmium	450 ml orthophosphoric acid 550 ml distilled water	Nickel	2†	5	30 min	20	Pot.	103	Electrodes horizontal.
Chromium	50 ml perchloric acid (sp. gr. 1·60) 1000 ml glacial acetic acid	Stainless steel	45-50* 24-28†	15-20	5-10 sec	20-30	Series	101	Longer times than 5 to 10 sec lead to passivity and etching of the specimen. Care must be taken when handling perchloric acid (see § 6). Range of voltage and current density not critical; polishing occurs up to 60 V†. If specimen is not entirely immersed, etched and unpolished areas occur at the air/solution interface. Chromium alloys, e.g. Vitallium,‡ can be polished under these conditions. Up to 15 ml water may be added after some use.
Cobalt	500 ml hydrochloric acid 500 ml ethyl alcohol	Stainless steel	8-9†	250	½-1½ min	20	Series	112	Bluish-green anodic film is soluble in water. Gives polished surface with slight grain boundary delineation and a good reaction to polarized light.
Cobalt	Orthophosphoric acid (sp. gr. 1·35)	Cobalt	1-1·5†	1-2	5-10 min	20	Pot.	114	Useful for production of strain-free surfaces for magnetic work. Produces slightly etched surfaces for metallographic studies. A solid black film forms during treatment and should be removed by wiping with cotton-wool. The c.d. then rises to 12 to 16 A/dm^2. At 1·65 to 1·70 V, the anode becomes completely passivated by a thick oxide layer.

Table 14. Copper

Composition	Cathode	Voltage	C.D. (A/dm²)	Time	Temp. (°C)	Circuit	Ref. No.	Remarks
700 ml orthophosphoric acid 350 ml distilled water	Copper	1·5-2†	6-8	15-30 min	20	Pot.	8	Polishes copper and many copper base alloys including α-, β- and α–β brasses, aluminium bronze, tin bronze, phosphor bronze, silicon bronze and copper alloys with low beryllium, iron, lead or cobalt content (of the order of 3 per cent). Small alterations in voltage are necessary to obtain optimum operating conditions for each alloy. To reduce pitting, anode can be removed and washed after 5 min electrolysis. "Polish-attack" is produced if solution is used with 7 to 10 V giving c.d. of 100 to 150 A/dm², and time is shorter (1 to 2 min) (see Fig. 2(d)).
670 ml orthophosphoric acid 100 ml sulphuric acid 300 ml distilled water	Copper	2-2·2†	10	15 min	20	Pot.	115	Polishes copper and alloys with up to 6 per cent tin. For higher tin contents, composition is altered to: 470 ml orthophosphoric acid 200 ml sulphuric acid 400 ml distilled water. When small amounts of phosphorus are present, an optically active surface, which reacts to polarized light, is produced.
350 ml orthophosphoric acid 620 ml ethyl alcohol	Copper	2-5‡	2-7	10-15 min	20	Pot.	116	For copper alloys with high lead content (up to 30 per cent lead).
Orthophosphoric acid (sp. gr. 1·04)	Copper	30*	30-60	1 min	20	Series	117	Produces "polish-attack" finish. Anode should be rotated in the electrolyte, which is cooled by running water.

* Voltage applied to circuit
† Approximate voltage drop across cell

Table 15. Gold, Hafnium and Indium

Metal	Composition	Cathode	Voltage	C.D. (A/dm²)	Time	Temp. (°C)	Circuit	Ref. No.	Remarks
Gold	67·5 g potassium cyanide 15 g potassium sodium tartrate 15 g potassium ferrocyanide 22·5 g phosphoric acid (solid) 2·5 ml ammonium hydroxide 1000 ml water	Stainless steel, carbon or platinum	9–10†	150	1–2 min	Above 60	Series	118	TOXIC solution; solution must be used under hood with good ventilation. Anode should be agitated rapidly in electrolyte. Solution decomposes rapidly and must be replenished frequently with fresh cyanide. Solution is erratic in operation. Has been used for copper–gold alloys [119]: 55–62°C, 1–4 min, Pt cathode, 4·5–5·0 V†, 100 A/dm². Solution must be discarded after 10 to 15 min.
Gold	75 g potassium cyanide 16 g potassium sodium tartrate 19 g potassium ferrocyanide 16 g phosphoric acid (solid) 4 g copper cyanide 3·5 ml ammonium hydroxide 1000 ml water	Stainless steel or carbon	Above 12†	150–200	1–2 min	About 60	Series	118	Same as solution above.
Hafnium	50–60 ml perchloric acid (sp. gr. 1·60) 1000 ml glacial acetic acid	Stainless steel	18†		5–10 sec	20	Series	120	Only used for wires (approx. 0·4 A for wires 0·08 to 0·2 in. dia.). Several successive immersions of a few seconds with continued agitation. Hafnium deforms readily and care should be taken in preparation.
Indium	330 ml nitric acid 670 ml methyl alcohol	Stainless steel	40–50*	30	1–2 min	20	Series	121	Used for polishing single crystals. Care should be taken when mixing this solution: add nitric acid slowly to cooled alcohol. Cool bath during use (see § 6.4).

* Voltage applied to circuit   † Approximate voltage drop across cell

Table 16. Iron

Composition	Cathode	Voltage	C.D. (A/dm²)	Time	Temp. (°C)	Circuit	Ref. No.	Remarks
50 ml perchloric acid (sp. gr. 1·60) 1000 ml glacial acetic acid	Stainless steel	45–60* 25–30†	40–80	15–30 sec	20–30	Series	101	Useful for pure iron and austenitic iron alloys. Care should be taken when handling perchloric acid (see § 6). Conditions are not critical, polishing occurring over a range of current densities. Not all the area immersed is polished if a vertical electrode is used; etched and un-attacked areas remain near the air/solution interface after treatment. A solid film sometimes forms on the surface during washing and can be removed with a dilute solution of hydrofluoric acid. Up to 15 ml water may be added to solution after some use.
185 ml perchloric acid (sp. gr. 1·61) 965 ml acetic anhydride 50 ml water	Iron or steel	40–50* 25–30†	4–6	8–15 min	Below 30	Series	98	Useful for preparation of strain-free surfaces on a large number of ferrous alloys. See § 6 for precautions with this type of solution. Efficiency of solution can be increased by initially dissolving about 0·5 per cent aluminium in the solution using an aluminium anode. Rate of stirring can then be increased to give more efficient cooling.
500 ml nitric acid 500 ml acetic anhydride	Iron or steel	110*	100–200	15–30 sec	20	Series	58	Care should be taken when mixing this solution; acetic anhydride should be added to cooled nitric acid (see § 6.4). Produces an excellent polish without attack on inclusions. Relative covering power is low and is only useful for small areas.

* Voltage applied to circuit
† Approximate voltage drop across cell

Table 16 (cont.) Iron

Composition	Cathode	Voltage	C.D. (A/dm²)	Time	Temp. (°C)	Circuit	Ref. No.	Remarks
60 ml perchloric acid (sp. gr. 1·54) 140 ml water 800 ml ethyl alcohol denatured with 3 per cent ether	Plain carbon or stainless steel	110–220* 35–70†	250–600	15–30 sec	Below 35	Series	10	Produces "polish-attack" and surface can be examined without further etching. The wide range of voltage and c.d. cover a wide range of ferrous alloys including plain C steels, high speed steels, 18/8 stainless steels, white cast iron and manganese steel. Conditions must be adjusted to give optimum operation for each alloy. Covering power is low and only small areas can be polished. Anode–cathode distance should be small. Care should be taken when handling perchloric acid (see § 6).
700 ml acetic anhydride 200 ml chromic acid‡ 100 ml water	Iron or steel	110*	100–200	15 sec– 2 min	20	Series	58	Very good polish on iron and all steels. The acetic anhydride should be carefully added, a drop at a time, to the cooled chromic acid, the water being added last (see § 6.4).
133 ml glacial acetic acid 25 g chromium trioxide 7 ml water	Stainless steel	50–60* 20–25†	10–15	6–8 min	20	Series	122	Used for production of strain-free surfaces for magnetic studies [32]. Solution should be cooled and anode rotated at 100 rev/min close to cathode. Water content is important since solution tends to absorb water readily. There are anomalies in the relation between cell resistance and cell voltage for this solution (see § 2.2).

* Voltage applied to circuit.　　† Approximate voltage drop across cell.　　‡ A 75 per cent solution of chromium trioxide in water.

Table 17. Lead

Composition	Cathode	Voltage	C.D. (A/dm²)	Time	Temp. (°C)	Circuit	Ref. No.	Remarks
350 ml perchloric acid (sp. gr. 1·61) 630 ml acetic anhydride 20 ml water	Lead or copper	50–70* 25–35†	9–12	5–10 min	Below 30	Series	95, 103	In order to avoid the excessive polishing time necessary to remove any deformed surface layer, an initial c.d. of 20 A/dm² should be used for approx. 1 min. Used for large strain-free surfaces.
200 ml perchloric acid (sp. gr. 1·20) 800 ml ethyl alcohol denatured with 3 per cent ether	Stainless steel	70–110* 15–35†	150–750	10–30 sec	Below 30	Series	10, 123	Produces "polish-attack" on many lead alloys. Wide range of conditions covers a wide range of alloys. Anode should be rotated close to the cathode for optimum operation. Recommended pre-treatment is to grind to 4/0 emery using white oil, and remove the oil with ether and alcohol prior to electrolysis.
200 ml fluoboric acid (comm.) 20 ml sulphuric acid 780 ml water	Stainless steel	50–60* 15–20†	400–700	3–5 sec	20–40	Series	124	The whole range of lead-tin alloys has been polished in this solution by suitable adjustment of the operating conditions. The solution is only useful for small areas, and a tilting cell has been used to reduce attack. As the specimen is immersed in the solution, the current falls off and a white streaming film forms on the anode. When a stable current value is reached, the specimen is removed and washed, since further electrolysis leads to heating and etching.
60 g anhydrous sodium acetate 315 ml glacial acetic acid 80 ml water	Carbon or platinum	50–60* 15–20†	7–12	4–10 min	20–30	Series	125	Cathode is placed ~5 cm away from vertical anode. Etching occurs at first, but after 4 min a highly reflecting surface appears.

* Voltage applied to circuit

† Approximate voltage drop across cell

Table 18. Magnesium

Composition	Cathode	Voltage	C.D. (A/dm²)	Time	Temp. (°C)	Circuit	Ref. No.	Remarks
350 ml ortho-phosphoric acid 625 ml ethyl alcohol	Stainless steel or nickel	1–2†	0·5	1 hr or more	20	Pot.	107, 116	Useful for preparing large strain-free surfaces. During mixing, alcohol should be added to cooled acid. The c.d. falls from 5 down to 0·5 A/dm² after 5 min and then stays constant. There is considerable initial gassing and after 5 min, anode should be shaken to remove any adhering bubbles. The long treatment time may be reduced by preliminary polishing with diamond dust. Washing should be rapid, since the free acid formed on hydrolysis tends to attack the Mg. Has been used for many magnesium alloys (see ref. 107, Pt. III, Chap. II and IX.)
400 ml ortho-phosphoric acid 380 ml absolute alcohol 250 ml distilled water	Magnesium	10†	20	2 min	20–50	Pot.	110	Useful for rapid specimen preparation. Temperature of solution need not be controlled. A solid film sometimes forms on washing and may be removed by swabbing with dilute nitric acid.
100 ml hydrochloric acid 900 ml ethylene glycol monoethyl ether	Stainless steel or nickel	10–15†	2	1–2 min	Below 10	Pot.	96	After initial polarization of anode, voltage is reduced to approx. 5 V with a c.d. of 1 A/dm². Surface gives good reaction to polarized light.
700 ml glacial acetic acid 300 ml perchloric acid (sp. gr. 1·60)	Stainless steel or nickel	20–30†	1·5	1–2 min	Below 30	Pot.	96	Precautions for perchloric acid solutions should be observed (see § 6).

† Approximate voltage drop across cell

Table 19. *Molybdenum and Nickel*

Metal	Composition	Cathode	Voltage	C.D. (A/dm²)	Time	Temp. (°C)	Circuit	Ref. No.	Remarks
Molybdenum *not* containing carbides	35 ml sulphuric acid 140 ml distilled water	Stainless steel	12*		25–35 sec	50	Series	126	A blue film of molybdic oxide covers the surface after polishing and this is removed by a 10 sec dip in conc. ammonium hydroxide.
Molybdenum containing carbides	50 ml hydrochloric acid 20 ml sulphuric acid 150 ml methyl alcohol	Stainless steel	24*	65–70	25–35 sec	50	Series	126	Used to prepare single crystals for studies of plastic deformation [127]. If solution becomes contaminated with water, a blue film of molybdic oxide is formed on specimen and carbides are attacked.
Molybdenum	25 ml sulphuric acid 175 ml methyl alcohol	Stainless steel		80–120	1 min	25		128	No agitation.
Nickel	210 ml perchloric acid (sp. gr. 1.61) 790 ml glacial acetic acid	Nickel or lead	110* 45–50†	40–80	2–3 min	Below 35	Series	95, 97	Care should be taken in handling this solution (see § 6). Polishing occurs with vigorous gas evolution.
Nickel	390 ml sulphuric acid 290 ml distilled water	Nickel	60*	39	4–6 min	Below 35	Series	129, 130	Care should be taken when mixing solution. Polishing occurs with vigorous gas evolution and anode should be rotated to reduce pitting. Operating conditions are not as critical as quoted, polishing occurring over a wide range of conditions.

* Voltage applied to circuit
† Approximate voltage drop across cell

Table 20. Niobium, Plutonium, Silver, Tantalum and Thorium

Metal	Composition	Cathode	Voltage	C.D. (A/dm²)	Time	Temp. (°C)	Circuit	Ref. No.	Remarks
Niobium	50 ml lactic acid 25 ml sulphuric acid 25 ml hydrofluoric acid (48 per cent)	Platinum	15–20†		5–10 min	20	Pot.	131	Solution should be stirred. Tendency to etching. Specimen should be prepared to fine finish prior to electrolysis.
Plutonium	50 ml orthophosphoric acid 50 ml di-ethylene glycol	Stainless steel	5†	Approx. 5	5–10 min	20	Pot.	131	Surface gives good reaction to polarized light, but oxidizes fairly rapidly in air.
Silver	35 g silver cyanide 37 g potassium cyanide 38 g potassium carbonate 1000 ml water	Silver	2·5–3·0†	Approx. 1	10 min	20	Pot.	132	Under these conditions, optimum polishing occurs in the region of voltage and current instability. Critical c.d. depends on concentration, temperature and stirring rate. Slow stirring should be used. Best polishing occurs with max. frequency of electrical oscillations (19). Other workers (133) have used 1·5 V (just below unstable region), and a c.d. of 1·1 A/dm² and time of 20 min. With horizontal anode, the under surface only is polished.
Niobium and Tantalum	90 ml sulphuric acid 10 ml hydrofluoric acid (48 per cent)	Platinum or carbon	50* 12–20†	10–20	5–10 min	35–45	Series	134, 135	Specimen may be etched using same solution at 2 A/dm² for 10 min. The temperature of the solution rises rapidly during operation and it may be necessary to cool the bath.
Thorium	20 ml perchloric acid (sp. gr. 1·64) 70 ml glacial acetic acid 5 ml water	Stainless steel		Approx. 60	7–12 sec	About 10	Series	136	Used for the examination of sintered powder compacts. Grain-contrast etch produced by treatment at 10 A/dm² for 30 to 45 sec.

* Voltage applied to circuit   † Approximate voltage drop across cell

Table 21. *Tin*

Composition	Cathode	Voltage	C.D. (A/dm²)	Time	Temp. (°C)	Circuit	Ref. No.	Remarks
Perchloric acid (sp. gr. 1·60)	Aluminium	50–60*	40	10–15 sec	Below 35	Series	100	Useful for preparation of strain-free surfaces but the marked "orange peel" effect on large areas makes it unsuitable for metallography. Surface has good reaction to polarized light. Care must be taken when handling perchloric acid (see § 6). Face to be polished should be vertical and rotated at 50–100 rev/min. Rate of dissolution is rapid and grain boundaries are etched.
63 ml perchloric acid (sp. gr. 1·48) 300 ml glacial acetic acid 13 ml water	Tin	20–30†	9–15	10 min	25	Pot.	103	Anode should be vertical and solution stirred. Care must be taken when handling perchloric acid solutions (see § 6).
200 ml fluoboric acid (comm.) 20 ml sulphuric acid 780 ml water	Stainless steel	15–17†	400–700	2–5 sec	20–40	Series	124	To reduce attack by solution, a tilting cell is used. White to grey sludge forms at low c.d., but a black, loosely adherent layer is present during polishing.
144 ml ethyl alcohol 10 g aluminium chloride (anhyd.) 45 g zinc chloride (anhyd.) 32 ml water 16 ml *n*-butyl alcohol	Tin or stainless steel	50–60* 25†	30	Periods of 1 min	20	Series	137, 138	4 cycles of 1 min are used. During the polishing cycle, a dark, sticky layer forms on the anode and this is removed by washing with a jet of hot water prior to next cycle. Useful for production of strain-free surfaces. Tendency to etching. Dilute alloys (0·5 atomic per cent Te, Al and Bi) were successfully polished; alloys with Sb did not polish. (See Table 26 for further remarks).

* Voltage applied to circuit

† Approximate voltage drop across cell

Table 22. Titanium and Tungsten

Metal	Composition	Cathode	Voltage	C.D. (A/dm²)	Time	Temp. (°C)	Circuit	Ref. No.	Remarks
Titanium	185 ml perchloric acid (sp. gr. 1·59) 795 ml acetic anhydride 48 ml water	Stainless steel	40–60*	20–30	Periods of 45–60 sec	Below 35	Series	99	Cathode vertical, but face to be polished should be horizontal, a few mm below the liquid level and should face the bottom of the cell. During electrolysis, anode tends to heat up and it is necessary to polish in periods of 45 to 60 sec. Specimen can be oxidized and examined under polarized light. Care should be taken when handling this solution (see § 6).
Titanium *not* containing carbides	60 ml perchloric acid (sp. gr. 1·54) 1000 ml glacial acetic acid	Titanium	30*	30–40	2 min	20	Series	103, 112, 139	Anode to cathode distance should be about 3 cm. Surfaces have good reaction to polarized light yielding marked grain contrast without further treatment.
Titanium	90 ml ethyl alcohol 10 ml n-butyl alcohol 6 g aluminium chloride (anhyd.) 28 g zinc chloride	Stainless steel	30–60* 20–25†		1–6 min	25	Series	140	Agitation is necessary to prevent formation of a passivating layer. Solution is stable for approx. a week. (See Table 26 for further remarks.)
Tungsten	100 g sodium hydroxide 1000 ml water	Stainless steel	6†	3–6	20–30 min	20	Pot.	141, 142	Rotation of anode or agitation of electrolyte with nitrogen is necessary.

* Voltage applied to circuit
† Approximate voltage drop across cell

Table 23. Uranium and Vanadium

Metal	Composition	Cathode	Voltage	C.D. (A/dm²)	Time	Temp. (°C)	Circuit	Ref. No.	Remarks
Uranium	100 ml orthophosphoric acid, 100 ml glycerol, 100 ml ethyl alcohol	Uranium, platinum or steel		10–20	30–40 min	20	Series	142	Solution should be cooled. Stirring is not necessary, but bath must be kept free of water, otherwise marked staining occurs.
Uranium	50 ml orthophosphoric acid, 100 ml sulphuric acid, 100 ml distilled water	Uranium or platinum		50–75	5–10 min	20	Series	142	More rapid polishing than with solution above. Flat, uniform surface produced and oxide particles not attacked. For best results, anodic layer should be continuously removed during polishing by wiping with a camel hair brush.
Uranium	50–100 ml perchloric acid (sp. gr. 1·60), 1000 ml glacial acetic acid	Stainless steel	50–60*, 10–20†	5–10	5 min	20	Series	102, 142	Contrast under polarized light is not as good as with the solutions above. Care must be taken when handling perchloric acid (see § 6).
Uranium	50 g chromium trioxide, 600 ml glacial acetic acid, 60 ml water	Uranium or platinum	30†		10–20 min	20	Pot.	143	If specimen is repolished for 3 to 5 min in same electrolyte cooled to 6 to 8°C, and then etched at 2 to 3 V for 8 to 12 min, subsequent atmospheric or anodic oxidation gives an epitaxial oxide layer sensitive to structural changes.
Vanadium	50–100 ml perchloric acid (sp. gr. 1·60), 950–900 ml glacial acetic acid	Stainless steel	50–60*, 25–30†	16–24	1–2 min	Below 35	Series	144	A second polishing period of about the same duration in a fresh solution is sometimes necessary. Solution tends to produce pitting. Care should be taken when handling perchloric acid (see § 6).

* Voltage applied to circuit † Approximate voltage drop across cell

Table 24. Zinc and Zirconium

Metal	Composition	Cathode	Voltage	C.D. (A/dm²)	Time	Temp. (°C)	Circuit	Ref. No.	Remarks
Zinc	200 g chromium trioxide 1000 ml water	Platinum, nickel or zinc	60*	250–350	40–45 sec	20	Series	145	Useful for rapid specimen preparation for studies of deformation [146]. The boundaries are etched slightly and the specimen is covered with a passive film which makes etching difficult.
Zinc	500 ml orthophosphoric acid 500 ml ethyl alcohol	Nickel or stainless steel	4–6* 2·5–3·5†	1·5–2·5	1 hour or more	20	Pot.	147	Excellent for preparation of surfaces for research. This solution is more concentrated than that originally proposed by JACQUET [116] viz. 375 ml orthophosphoric acid, 625 ml ethyl alcohol. Difficulties arose with Jacquet's solution due to film formation on washing. An initial high current at the anode may lead to the formation of gas bubbles which should be shaken off. Has been used for studies of recrystallization using polarized light [148]. The long time of treatment may be reduced by preliminary polishing with diamond dust.
Zirconium	50–100 ml perchloric acid (sp. gr. 1·60) 1000 ml glacial acetic acid	Stainless steel	40–50* 12–18†	15	45 sec	Below 30	Pot.	99, 149	Some etching and slight relief produced. Specimen should be rotated during polishing. After removal from solution specimen should be rinsed in 2 to 4 ml glacial acetic acid in 50 ml water.
Zirconium	50 ml perchloric acid 175 ml glacial acetic acid 100 ml ethylene glycol	Stainless steel	30–50*	Above 100	20–30 sec	Below 30	Series	112	Suitable for examination using polarized light.

* Voltage applied to circuit   † Approximate voltage drop across cell

Table 25. Special Alloys

Metal	Composition	Cathode	Voltage	C.D. (A/dm²)	Time	Temp. (°C)	Circuit	Ref. No.	Remarks
Light alloys particularly of Al–Zn–Mg type	100–300 g chromic acid (anhyd.) 100 ml orthophosphoric acid	Stainless steel	3–12†	7–50		50–90	Pot.	101	The working conditions extend over a wide range and particular conditions need to be developed for different compositions. After polishing specimens can be anodized at 50 to 60°C for 1 to 2 min to give interference colours which reveal the structure.
Manganese-copper alloys (>82 wt. % Mn)	100 ml orthophosphoric acid 100 ml glycerol 200 ml absolute alcohol	Stainless steel	18†	28		20	Series	150	A suitable etchant is 5 per cent citric acid.
Nimonic or nickel-chromium alloys	450 ml glacial acetic acid 40 ml perchloric acid (sp. gr. 1·60) 15 ml distilled water	Stainless steel	50–60* 15†	Approx. 10	3–4 min	25	Series	151	Anode-cathode distance should be about 3 cm.
Nimonic or nickel-chromium alloys	150 ml sulphuric acid 640 ml orthophosphoric acid 210 ml water	Stainless steel	2·5–2·8†	60–75	5 min	Approx. 70	Pot.	152	Can also be used for chromium and chromium alloys (153) when the conditions are less critical e.g. 20–120°C, 2·5–18 V† (slow fluctuations occur within these limits), 150–250 A/dm².

* Voltage applied to circuit
† Approximate voltage drop across cell

Table 25 (cont.) Special Alloys

Metal	Composition	Cathode	Voltage	C.D. (A/dm²)	Time	Temp. (°C)	Circuit	Ref. No.	Remarks
Vitallium	Up to 84 wt. per cent ethylene glycol 5–22 wt. per cent sulphuric acid 0·25–5 wt. per cent hydrochloric acid Remainder water (below 8 wt. per cent)	Stainless steel		8–80		20–55	Series	154	Typical composition is: 910 ml ethylene glycol 310 ml sulphuric acid 5 ml hydrochloric acid 20 ml water Used for Ni–Cr–Be and Co–Cr–Mo alloys.
Vitallium	60 ml sulphuric acid 60 ml orthophosphoric acid 60 ml ethyl alcohol 60 ml water 270 ml ethylene glycol	Stainless steel or copper	12–15* 7–9†	10–15	10–20 min	50–60	Pot.	29	The solution tends to become green in colour during operation but this does not appear to affect the efficiency. The film on the specimen is readily soluble in water.
Tungsten carbide	20 g sodium hydroxide 30 g sodium tungstate 1000 ml water	Copper or carbon	21†	400	2 min	20	Series	155	Used for W–C–Co alloys.

* Voltage applied to circuit
† Approximate voltage drop across cell

Table 26. Electrolytes of General Use

Composition	Cathode	Voltage	C.D. (A/dm²)	Time	Temp. (°C)	Circuit	Ref. No.	Remarks
144 ml ethyl alcohol 10 g aluminium chloride (anhyd.) 45 g zinc chloride 32 ml water 16 ml n-butyl alcohol	Stainless steel	40–60* 15–25†	5–30	see "Remarks"	20	Pot.	137	There are two methods of using this solution: 1. Cyclic treatment involving approx. 1 min of electrolysis and then washing with hot water. This is necessary to remove the dark passivating layer which forms on the anode in the absence of agitation. This cyclic treatment is continued until the desired polish is obtained. Under these conditions the process is only suitable for small areas due to the poor current distribution. 2. Rapid oscillation of the anode in a vertical plane at a fixed distance from the cathode (1 to 2 cm) hinders the formation of the passivating layer and polishing can proceed as a continuous process for 3 to 6 min with an improved current distribution. Both these methods have been used for aluminium and its alloys, cobalt, nickel, stainless steel, tin, titanium and zinc [91, 137, 140].
100 ml nitric acid 200 ml methyl alcohol	Stainless steel	40–50*	100–200	½–1 min	20	Series	156	Has been used for aluminium, copper and copper alloys, indium, iron and steels, nickel and nickel alloys, and zinc [91, 121, 156]. Limitations are: (a) the explosive nature of solution (see § 6·4). It is necessary to cool the solution with an ice bath and polish for short periods only. (b) the rapidity of attack. It is possible to control the polishing in some cases, e.g. aluminium, by using a lower current density of 10 A/dm².

* Voltage applied to circuit   † Approximate voltage drop across cell

Table 26 (cont.) Electrolytes of General Use

Composition	Cathode	Voltage	C.D. (A/dm²)	Time	Temp. (°C)	Circuit	Ref. No.	
200 ml perchloric acid (sp. gr. 1·20) 800 ml ethyl alcohol	Stainless steel or copper	110* 35–70†	100–400	10–30 sec	35	Series	10	The recommended sp. gr. of the perchloric acid varies from 1·12 to 1·25 but does not seem to be critical. Has been used for aluminium and alloys, cast irons and steels, lead and lead alloys, nickel alloys, tin, Vitallum and zinc and zinc alloys [10, 109, 123]. Limitation is that the process is a "polish-attack" method i.e. gives an etched surface, and is only suitable for small areas. Rapid agitation is necessary because of rapid temperature rise at anode. Modifications of this solution are used in the "Disa-Electropol" apparatus (see § 5·2) e.g. 200 ml perchloric acid (sp. gr. 1·20) 100 ml glycerine 700 ml ethyl alcohol.

* Voltage applied to circuit
† Approximate voltage drop across cell

CHAPTER 8

INDUSTRIAL APPLICATIONS OF ELECTROLYTIC POLISHING

8.1. GENERAL PRINCIPLES FOR INDUSTRIAL METHODS

THE principles involved in electropolishing on a laboratory scale apply to electropolishing on an industrial scale, although modifications in technique are necessary when large areas are involved and continuous production is to be carried out.

Solutions—From an economic point of view, the types of polishing solution used in industry can be divided into two classes:

(1) those possessing "infinitely" long useful life where
 (a) metal is deposited on the cathode at the same rate as it is dissolved from the anode, or
 (b) insoluble metal salts precipitate without hindering operations and are periodically filtered off;

(2) those which have to be discarded or regenerated when the metal concentration builds up to a point where it prevents satisfactory polishing.

Usually little metal is removed during industrial electropolishing (of the order of 25 microns) and large areas of metal can be polished before a solution must be discarded. Detailed procedures have been given for the regeneration of the sulphuric acid–phosphoric acid–chromic acid solutions used for electropolishing steels [157].

In general, the solutions used in industry are good conductors and thus the potential drop across a cell is small. However, the series circuit is generally used since the currents involved are high and the power loss would be considerable with a potentiometric circuit (see Fig. 9). The anode current density is used to control the process and the voltages quoted in § 9 are the approximate cell voltages obtained under operating conditions. The electrical conditions depend on the electrolyte, size of the electrodes and the tank, agitation and solution temperature, but, in general, cell voltages between 5 and 15 V at 10 to 40 A/dm² (100 to 500 A/ft²) are used. In order to avoid over-heating, currents are normally limited to 1·5 to 3 A per litre of solution, although up to 6 A per litre has been used.

Agitation—Many industrial solutions operate under conditions of gas evolution and therefore agitation is an important factor in the process. The conditions of agitation must be adjusted so as to prevent the gas discharged at the surface of the anode from producing pitting and streaking [158]. Agitation is usually effected by applying a simple oscillating motion to the racks carrying the articles to be polished or by bubbling air through the solution [Fig. 28(a)].

Temperature—The temperatures used are generally in the range of 45 to 65°C (113 to 149°F) but, in some cases, operation is carried out at 85°C (185°F). Suitable heating arrangements must be used to control the temperature of the bath within the given range for any solution.

Washing—To ensure an even polish, the articles should be degreased, either by vapour or aqueous alkaline solution, rinsed and nearly completely dried prior to electropolishing. After treatment, the articles should be rinsed again and then water-sprayed prior to final drying.

Tanks—All concentrations of acids used in electropolishing solutions and in rinses can be handled in tanks lined with lead. Electropolishing solutions containing more than 30 per cent water can be handled for long periods, when cool, in cast iron equipment. Tanks lined with "chemical" lead are most widely used, although tanks lined with certain synthetic resins, e.g. polythene, are also used. At temperatures below their softening points these resins are resistant to many of the solutions in commercial use.

Racks—Copper is the most suitable material for construction of racks to support articles during polishing. Since copper is attacked only slowly, bare racks can be used, but a better practice is to insulate them with an inert coating. The part of the work in contact with the rack should be clean and the contact should be made securely to prevent arcing.

Control of Electrolyte Composition—With a continuous process the composition of the electrolyte often changes considerably so that it is necessary to carry out frequent measurement and adjustment of specific gravity, viscosity and ratio of component acids. A simple method of analysis for sulphuric acid-orthophosphoric acid solutions is given in Appendix III.

Usually, any plant equipped for electroplating or anodizing can be employed for electropolishing, since the requirements for racking and current distribution are similar for the three processes (Fig. 28).

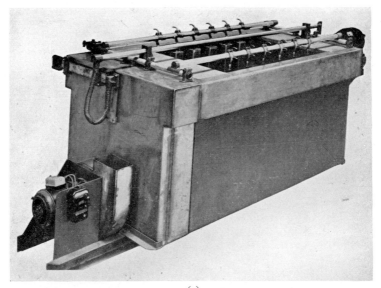

(a)

(b)   *(Courtesy of* Dr. R. Mondon)

Fig. 28.   Industrial electropolishing equipment:
(a) Typical tank of 500 l. capacity with provision for agitation by
oscillation of anode racks;
(b) Installation for electromachining of gear wheels.

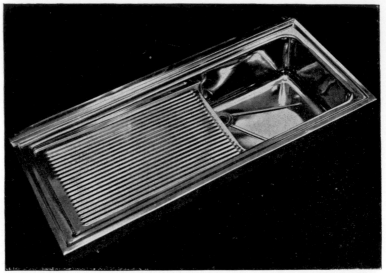

Fig. 30. Stainless steel sink finished by electropolishing.

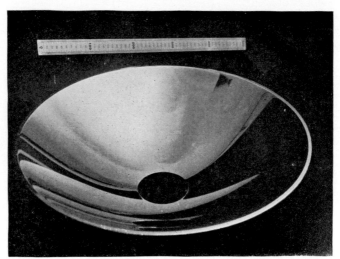

Fig. 31. Parabolic mirror of pure aluminium finished by electropolishing and then anodically oxidized.

A layout for a practical production line for brass cruets which incorporates electropolishing has been given by BERGER [159] and, although not representative of present-day practice, it illustrates nevertheless most of the points that have been discussed so far. A schematic layout of this plant is shown in Fig. 29.

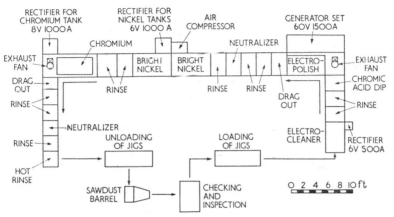

Fig. 29. Schematic layout of plant used by BERGER [159] for the electropolishing of brass articles on an industrial scale.

8.2. APPLICATIONS OF ELECTROLYTIC POLISHING

The commercial possibilities of electropolishing are indicated by the many applications of this technique recorded in the technical literature [160–164]. The most common applications are discussed in detail below.

8.2.1. Finishing operations

The development of electropolishing as an industrial method of finishing is due to the economic and technical advantages which it presents. For example, the extensive manual operations needed in mechanical polishing are reduced, metals such as stainless steel which are difficult to polish mechanically can be electropolished easily and articles of complex shape can be treated readily by a suitable arrangement of cathodes [165].

In order to produce the best results the metal must be homogeneous and free from surface defects. Defects which are normally hidden by mechanical polishing may be revealed, or even exaggerated, by electropolishing, e.g. inclusions, casting irregularities, seams, etc.

will be eliminated if they are near the surface, but are exaggerated if they lie at a critical distance from the surface. This critical distance is the average depth of metal removed during polishing. The polish obtained depends greatly on the purity of the metal, e.g. 99·98 per cent aluminium can be given a mirror finish, but the quality of the polish decreases as the impurity content increases. The grain size of the metal also influences the quality of the polish, e.g. with large grained material, some differential solution occurs leading to an uneven surface. The best results are obtained with fine grained sheet produced by repeated cold working and annealing. HERENGUEL and SEGOND [166] give details of the strict control needed during the manufacture of aluminium–magnesium alloys to obtain satisfactory electropolishing of formed articles.

The type of finish produced by electropolishing is entirely different from that produced by mechanical polishing, since the fine scratches from polishing grit are not present to cause diffraction of light. Thus, a large, flat surface that has been electropolished does not have the mirror-like appearance of the mechanically polished article. In general, the reflected images from industrially electropolished surfaces are not as sharp as those from mechanically polished surfaces, and there is a tendency to reject the finish as unsatisfactory because of the difficulty in focusing an image. Electropolishing shows to the best advantage on parts where curved surfaces help to break up the reflection of light so that defects in the metal are not emphasized and the observer does not expect to see a sharp image. (See, for example, Figs. 30 and 31).

8.2.2. Machining operations [164, 165, 167]

The electropolishing process can be used as a machining operation by using suitable conditions and auxiliary cathodes to control the rate at which metal is removed from the surface of the anode. This operation, known as "electromachining" or "electrolytic superfinishing," has been developed in France and applied widely in the aircraft engine industry (Fig. 32). As well as improving the surface finish, the treatment removes deformed surface zones produced by previous machining operations and reveals any defects in the metal, such as inclusions or cracks, caused by poor heat treatment or incorrect grinding. The ability to reveal fine surface imperfections has led to the use of electropolishing as a routine inspection method in cases where 100 per cent inspection is necessary,

Fig. 32. Crankshaft of 4-cylinder Diesel engine after
electromachining of journals and shaft.

Fig. 33. Mating gearwheels with teeth profiles
produced by electromachining.

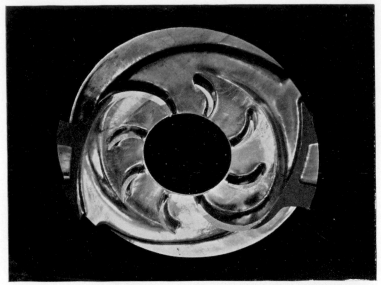

(*Courtesy of* Dr. R. Mondon)

Fig. 34. Component of feed pump, made from cast 13 per cent chromium steel, after electromachining of internal surfaces.

ø 235

(*Courtesy of* Dr. R. Mondon

Fig. 35. Component of flame tube for gas turbine after electrolytic deburring of air entry holes.

e.g. turbine blades for jet engines. Further, since the rate of metal removal can be controlled accurately, it is possible to produce shapes which are difficult or even impossible to produce by mechanical methods. An example of this application is the forming of special profiles for gear teeth (Fig. 33). By adjusting the throwing power of the electrolyte, internal surfaces which are difficult to polish mechanically can be electromachined to fine limits (Fig. 34). Further, there are many instances where sawing, grinding and stamping burrs can be removed more economically by electropolishing than by mechanical methods (Fig. 35). The corrosion resistance of metals is improved by electrolytic superfinishing, probably due both to removal of deformed surface zones with their local potential differences, and to the presence of a passivating film after treatment.

At first sight, it would appear that electromachining would be an ideal method of raising the fatigue strength of metals. However, although such an effect has been claimed [167], it appears that the fatigue limit is usually lowered by such treatment. This may be due to the removal from the surface of the compressive stresses produced by previous finishing operations [168, 169]. If electropolishing is used as a finishing operation, a light mechanical treatment, e.g. shot peening, will restore the fatigue properties. The "notch effect" of inclusions on the fatigue limit is usually accentuated by electropolishing due to differential rates of dissolution around inclusions (see § 4.3).

8.2.3. Surface preparation and electroplating

Electropolishing can be fitted into the electroplating production line to allow continuous operation, since the polishing of the basis metal, the brightening of the intermediate deposits and the final plating may be carried out with the article still in the same rack (see § 8.1). If a metal surface is electropolished prior to heavy electroplating, the bond obtained is much stronger than that with a mechanically polished surface, due to better continuity across the bulk metal/plated layer interface. In one instance, a thick deposit of nickel on a machined mild steel specimen had an adhesion of 16 tons/in^2 and fracture occurred in the surface layers of the steel. However, with an electropolished mild steel specimen the adhesion was 45 tons/in^2 and fracture occurred within the deposit[160].

In decorative finishing the final operation often involves the plating of a very thin layer of some non-tarnishing material to protect the object from corrosion. If the object is electropolished prior to this plating, a thin layer can be deposited which retains the brightness of the polished surface and thus eliminates final buffing. However, electropolished metals often have a passive film on the surface after treatment, and this film can reduce adhesion considerably. In such cases the film must be removed by a suitable etching treatment prior to electroplating.

Electrolytic polishing allows controlled dissolution of metal so that the metal removed can be replaced by the same thickness of plating. This is particularly important for machine parts built up by hard chromium plating. FAUST [161] gives an example of automatic machining where steel and brass screws, which are required to be electroplated without disturbing the original code size, are electropolished and then brought back to the original dimensions by plating.

8.2.4. Electrolytic polishing as an intermediate stage in production

Besides replacing mechanical finishing processes, electrolytic polishing can be used as an intermediate stage in production. HALUT [167] gives an example where nickel–silver spoons after blanking were electropolished and then stamped and pressed. A perfect surface finish was then obtained with one light buff. Without electropolishing, the same spoons required three mechanical polishing operations and final buffing.

JACQUET [61] has pointed out that electrolytic polishing of metals may increase their capacity for plastic deformation. For example, electrolytic polishing of nickel–silver prior to swaging eliminated three intermediate annealing operations, while molybdenum after electrolytic polishing could be drawn into the most complicated shapes. Further, electrolytic polishing of chromium and chromium-base alloys, hitherto considered brittle when untreated or etched surfaces were used, resulted in a marked improvement in ductility [153]. Such effects are due to the removal of surface defects produced during previous treatment and, in the case of metals having a ductile-brittle transition, to a reduction of surface roughness with consequent reduction of the "notch effect".

CHAPTER 9

INDUSTRIAL METHODS FOR SPECIFIC METALS AND THEIR ALLOYS

THERE are many electropolishing solutions which produce excellent results on the laboratory scale, but on a production scale only a few solutions are of economic interest and most of the successful commercial methods have been patented. Patents have been listed where possible, but the patent rights should be investigated fully prior to any commercial application of processes described in this chapter.

A full discussion of industrial methods for stainless steel, nickel, aluminium, carbon steels, copper and brass is given by WERNICK [162] and the reader is referred to his book for further details of processes and patents.

9.1. ALUMINIUM AND ALUMINIUM ALLOYS

The industrial polishing of aluminium and aluminium alloys has been discussed thoroughly by JACQUET [107] and WERNICK and PINNER [173]; only the essential details will be given here. Three main processes have been developed, viz. the Brytal, Alzak and Battelle processes. These processes are designed as finishing treatments and strictly should be called "brightening" processes, since very little metal is removed. They are used mainly on articles manufactured from rolled or mechanically polished sheet. All three processes consist of two stages: a polishing treatment followed by an anodizing treatment to reinforce the oxide film and prevent corrosion.

The Brytal process [107, 170, 171]

This process has been developed by the British Aluminium Co. and the details of the polishing treatment are:

Solution:	150 g sodium carbonate (anhyd.)
	50 g trisodium phosphate
	1000 ml water
Cathode:	Mild steel (preferably 5 : 1 ratio of cathode/ anode area)
Voltage:	10

Current   An initial c.d. of 4·3 to 5·4 A/dm² (40 to
density: 50 A/ft²) falling to 2·5 to 3 A/dm² (23 to
                 29 A/ft²) during polishing
Time: 8–10 min
Temperature: 78–82°C (172–180°F)

A bath in good working condition should have pH 10·5 [170] and some difficulty has been experienced in polishing outside the range pH 10 to 10·5 [171]. Since the solution is strongly alkaline the article should be washed rapidly in cold water to prevent attack by the electrolyte after polishing. For very pure metal, the time of polishing can be decreased to less than 8 min.

The anodizing treatment, to stabilize the oxide film, may be carried out under the following conditions:

Solution: 250 g sodium bisulphite
                 1000 ml water
Cathode: Stainless steel
Voltage: 12
Current
density: 0·65–0·87 A/dm² (6–8 A/ft²)
Time: 20–30 min
Temperature: 20°C (68°F)

It is now more usual to anodize using a dilute sulphuric acid solution similar to that described for the Alzak process. The anode is removed, washed in cold water and the film finally sealed by immersion in distilled water at 80 to 85°C (176 to 185°F) for 10 min. This treatment makes the film somewhat opaque and the original transparency can be restored by immersion in 10 per cent sulphuric acid at room temperature for several minutes. The article is then washed in cold water and dried.

The Alzak process [172]

The Aluminum Co. of America has developed a process using fluoboric acid and the conditions for the polishing treatment are:

Solution: 25 g fluoboric acid
                 1000 ml water
Cathode: Aluminium or copper
Voltage: 10–25
Current
density: 2–6 A/dm² (18·5–55·5 A/ft²)

Time: 5–10 min
Temperature: 30°C (86°F)

The electrolyte is prepared by dissolving 40 g boric acid in 100 g hydrofluoric acid, the mixture is then allowed to cool and is diluted in the ratio of 1 : 20 with water to reach the working concentration of 2·5 per cent. Since the solution is corrosive it should be kept in a rubber-lined tank. Considerable heat is evolved during operation and it is necessary to use copper cooling coils which may also be used as the cathode.

For anodizing, the following conditions are used:

Solution: 70 ml sulphuric acid
                 930 ml water
Cathode: Stainless steel
Voltage: 20
Current
  density: 1·3 A/dm² (12 A/ft²)
Time: 10–20 min
Temperature: 20°C (68°F)

After anodizing, the film is sealed by immersion in water at 80–100°C (176–212°F) for 10 min.

The Battelle processes [173, 174]

The Battelle Memorial Institute has developed a range of solutions based on orthophosphoric acid to which sulphuric acid is added to lower the resistance of the cell. By an alteration of composition these solutions can be used both for brightening and smoothing treatments.

One solution which has been used for finishing treatments is:

Solution: 400 ml sulphuric acid
                 600 ml orthophosphoric acid
                 10 ml glycerine
Cathode: Stainless steel
Voltage: 5–15
Current
  density: 11–16 A/dm² (100–150 A/ft²)
Time: 15 min
Temperature: 60°C (140°F)

After polishing, the article is rinsed in cold water and anodized in a 10 per cent solution of sulphuric acid as described previously.

Details of two of the solutions which can be used to replace mechanical polishing prior to anodizing and dyeing are listed below. These solutions produce a marked smoothing but the reflectivity of the polished surface is poorer than with the brightening treatment described above.

	A	B	
Solution:	47	140 ml sulphuric acid	
	750	570 ml orthophosphoric acid	
	65	90 ml chromic acid	
	45	– ml combined dissolved trivalent aluminium and trivalent chromium	
	93	200 ml water	
Cathode:	Stainless steel		
Voltage:	7–15		
Current density:	6·5–16 A/dm² (60–150 A/ft²)		
Time:	10–15 min		
Temperature:	70–95°C (160–200°F)		

These solutions should be agitated mechanically during use. The chromium passivates the aluminium when the current is switched off and thus etching is avoided during the rinsing operation. The maximum permissible aluminium content for satisfactory operation falls off rapidly when the sulphuric acid content exceeds 5 to 7 per cent, and thus solution B has a shorter working life than solution A. The preparation of such solutions is described fully in § 9.2.

9.2. COPPER AND COPPER ALLOYS

The electrolytes which have been developed for metallographic work with copper and its alloys are not suitable for industrial use. The orthophosphoric acid process, which operates under viscous layer conditions, has poor covering power for large articles, since the viscous layer does not penetrate into corners and tends to stream off the vertical sections. On the other hand, the chromic acid process, which operates under conditions of vigorous gas evolution, has good covering power but the low rate of metal removal produces a poor finish. Furthermore, the high current density required is uneconomical.

The Battelle Memorial Institute has developed a modified ortho-phosphoric acid electrolyte [175] and the operating conditions are:

Solution: 75–84 wt. per cent orthophosphoric acid
3–15 wt. per cent trivalent aluminium
0–2·0 wt. per cent trivalent chromium
Remainder water
Cathode: Copper or stainless steel
Voltage: 4–5
Current
density: 5–11 A/dm² (50–100 A/ft²)
Time: 10–15 min
Temperature: 0–38°C (30–100°F)

The solution may be prepared in either of two ways. In the first, the theoretical amount of metallic aluminium is dissolved in ortho-phosphoric acid. The trivalent chromium salt, preferably chromic chloride, is then added and the solution heated for some time to remove the chlorine. This is a lengthy operation and must be carried out in a fume cupboard using small amounts of solution. In the second way, the theoretical amount of chromic acid is dissolved in the orthophosphoric acid, the aluminium is added and the solution electrolyzed until the chromium has been reduced to the trivalent state. After use, 0·3 to 1·0 wt. per cent of copper tends to build up in the solution, but the bath may be operated continuously and requires only specific gravity control, occasional analysis and re-placement of "dragout" losses. The copper is deposited on the cathode as a fine powder of less than 10 microns in size and is useful for powder metallurgy.

A wide range of single phase copper–zinc alloys can be polished successfully under almost the same conditions, the best results being obtained with "cartridge brass" and "gilding metal." Leaded brasses cannot be polished successfully because the discrete particles of lead do not dissolve during electrolysis (see § 4.3). Polished brass articles should be thoroughly rinsed in water, and dipped in a 1 per cent nitric acid solution to prevent staining by phosphate films.

A simple solution for polishing brass has been described by MAZIA [89]. Details of this treatment are as follows:

Solution: 950 ml orthophosphoric acid
50 ml sulphuric acid

Cathode: Copper sheet or tubing preferably coated with
                a tin–lead alloy, lead or speculum.
Voltage: 5–10
Current
  density: 22–65 A/dm² (200–500 A/ft²)
Time: 10–15 min
Temperature: 60–65°C (140–150°F)

The type of temperature control used in chromium plating tanks
is suitable for this solution. The cathode area should be at least
20 times the anode area.

BERGER [159] gives details of the development of a suitable
solution for brass, his final process being:

Solution: 100–300 ml orthophosphoric acid
                700–900 ml water
                420 g/l sodium chromate
                80–85 g/l sulphuric acid
                180 g/l chromium trioxide
                3–6 g/l hydrofluoric acid
                80–150 g/l propionic acid
Cathode: Copper
Voltage: 14
Current
  density: 15–38 A/dm² (140–350 A/ft²)
Time: 5–10 min
Temperature: 15–49°C (60–120°F, optimum about 75°F)

If this solution is used prior to plating, the articles should be rinsed
in a neutralizing solution to remove any trace of salts formed by
hydrolysis of the anodic film during washing, Berger found that the
maximum flat area which could be polished was about 0·6 dm² (9 in²)
but if the surface of the article was interrupted by patterns, holes
etc., treatment was successful up to a limit of more than 6·5 dm²
(100 in²). Berger discusses the use of addition agents to improve
the brightness of the final surface and the "throwing power" of the
electrolyte. AXTELL [176] describes another electrolyte for brass,
also based on orthophosphoric acid, in which ethylene glycol,
lactic acid, glutamic acid and/or glycine are used for similar reasons.
Further research on the role of addition agents in electropolishing
may lead to improvement of many other industrial electrolytes.

9.3. CHROMIUM

Although the electropolishing of large areas of chromium plate is not yet a commercial proposition, small parts built up with chromium plate and dentures made from chromium alloys can be finished by electropolishing c.f. [154]. The increasing use of chromium alloys in gas turbines should lead to a large scale application of electropolishing as a machining and as a finishing process, c.f. [164]. Processes using sulphuric acid–orthophosphoric acid solutions (Table 25) seem most suitable for industrial use.

9.4. GOLD

Electropolishing should prove useful for gold and gold alloys used in the jewellery trade, particularly on articles with fine filigree work, when mechanical polishing is tedious and costly. The processes given in Table 15 seem suitable for production purposes, provided that the recommended precautions are taken.

9.5. FERROUS ALLOYS

Most of the research on industrial electropolishing has been directed to the polishing of iron and its alloys, particularly stainless steels and irons, since these are difficult to polish by mechanical methods. It is convenient to discuss plain carbon and low alloy steels separately from the stainless steels.

(a) Plain carbon and low-alloy steels

Perchloric acid solutions are not generally employed for commercial electropolishing of steels because of potential hazards associated with their use (see § 6) but in Germany some forty or so plants with baths containing up to 1200 l. of solution are in operation. These plants are carefully controlled and fitted with devices which immediately introduce water in the bath if the temperature rises dangerously [177]. Elsewhere, perchloric acid solutions are used only for finishing small hardened tools and dies for precision work, and industrial research has been directed to finding other acid mixtures.

Since plain carbon and low alloy steels usually contain some inclusions and defects, the process is generally used for machining, for burr removal and in preparation for plating, painting and vitreous enamelling rather than for finishing for appearance.

For large articles, the best results have been obtained with solutions of the orthophosphoric acid–sulphuric acid type [158]. A typical solution is:

Solution:	300 ml sulphuric acid
	600 ml orthophosphoric acid
	150 ml water
	35 ml dextrose *or* 0·9 ml "Teepol"
Cathode:	Stainless steel
Voltage:	7–8·5
Current	
density:	2·7–6·5 A/dm^2 (25–60 A/ft.^{2})
Time:	10 min
Temperature:	60–70°C (140–158°F)

The maximum permissible free water content of the solution is approximately 30 per cent and the minimum for satisfactory working is approximately 9 per cent. With these conditions, the mean surface roughness can be reduced from 400 microns to 37 microns. This solution gives rise to severe "grooving" with vertical electrodes unless the anode carrier is agitated, since the gas bubbles tend to rise close to the anode surface, disturb the viscous layer and thus upset the current distribution.

Alloying constituents do not cause any trouble except in the case of high carbon steels containing tungsten. Steels containing the following alloying constituents have been polished satisfactorily with the solution given above:

Nickel	up to a maximum of 3·75 per cent,
Molybdenum	up to a maximum of 0·5 per cent,
Chromium	up to a maximum of 1·4 per cent,
Manganese	up to a maximum of 1·75 per cent,
Vanadium	up to a maximum of 0·3 per cent.

Orthophosphoric acid–chromic acid solutions have also been used for plain carbon and low alloy steels. The times of treatment range from a ½ to 1 hr and initially the solutions give brilliant mirror-like finishes. However, after the solution has been used for some time, the finish tends to deteriorate due to chemical reduction of the chromic acid.

Orthophosphoric acid, saturated with chromic acid, is used for electrolytic superfinishing [162, 164]. The current densities for this operation are extremely high (up to 100 A/dm²) with a treatment time of approximately 1 min.

(b) Stainless steels

Mechanical polishing of stainless steel is particularly difficult and involves long and costly grinding and buffing operations. Electropolishing has proved to be cheaper than mechanical polishing and produces a surface with a better reflectivity. CHARLESWORTH and HOBSON [163] give examples where stainless steel articles with areas of 50 ft² or more (up to 250 ft² in one case) have been polished successfully [see, for example, Fig. 30].

A wide variety of electrolytes have been proposed and patented for polishing stainless steel [161, 178] but only a few of these are economic and practicable. Orthophosphoric acid–sulphuric acid solutions are the most suitable, but citric acid–sulphuric acid solutions have also been used. One of the most satisfactory methods for stainless steels [179, 180] uses the following conditions:

Solution:	300 ml orthophosphoric acid
	530 ml glycerine (sp. gr. 1·26)
	90 ml water
Cathode:	Stainless steel
Voltage:	4–5 V for new solution, but on ageing rises to 7–8 V
Current density:	7·8 A/dm² (72 A/ft.²)
Time:	15 min
Temperature:	110 ± 5°C (230 ± 9°F)

At the operating temperature the evaporation losses are high and these, together with the "dragout" losses, must be replaced from time to time.

An orthophosphoric acid–sulphuric acid solution has been used successfully for stainless steel and may be modified, with excellent results, for plain carbon steels by the addition of 10 wt. per cent of chromic acid [89, 181]:

Solution:	125 ml sulphuric acid
	650 ml orthophosphoric acid
	225 ml water

Cathode: Copper sheet or tubing preferably coated to prevent corrosion
Voltage: 8–15 V
Current
  density: 7·8–22·5 A/dm² (72–216 A/ft.²)
Time: 5–10 min
Temperature: 82–88°C (180–190°F)

The process is usually controlled by analysis of the solution for sulphuric acid, orthophosphoric acid and iron. A simple procedure for estimating sulphuric and orthophosphoric acid contents is given in Appendix III. The dissolved metal content rises by about 1 wt. per cent iron per 30,000 A hr/500 l. and limit is reached when the iron content exceeds approximately 4 per cent.

Another successful commercial solution [182] is:

Solution: 110 ml sulphuric acid
                  600 g citric acid
                  250 ml methyl alcohol
Cathode: Stainless steel
Voltage: 6–8
Current
  density: 8–55 A/dm² (72–500 A/ft²)
Time: 1–3 min
Temperature: 50–125°C (122–257°F)

The methyl alcohol can be replaced by butyl, propyl or ethyl alcohols or glycerol. Although the solution is expensive it has a long life since the metal salts precipitate and can be removed.

It is important to realize that some stainless steels polish much better than others and this must be taken into account in the design of stainless steel articles for electropolishing. An 18 per cent nickel, 8 per cent chromium steel gives the best results [161]. Further, when austenitic stainless steel has been made susceptible to corrosion by faulty heat treatment, it will not polish as smoothly as steel in the entirely austenitic state. Table 27 shows the effect of various alloying additions on the degree of polish obtainable with 18/8 stainless steel.

In modified stainless steel, the particles of complex carbides do not polish at the same rate as the austenitic matrix and therefore are left in relief.

Table 27. Effect of Alloying Elements on the Polish Obtainable with 18/8 Stainless Steel

No.	Additional element (wt. per cent)	Degree of polish
1	None	Good
2	More that 0·5 copper	Good but inferior to No. 1
3	Copper 0·5, tungsten 0·5 to 1, titanium 1	Fair but some etching occurs
4	Copper 0·5, tungsten 1	Medium
5	Molybdenum 3 to 4	Medium but a "bloom" is present

9.6. MAGNESIUM

Although a method of polishing magnesium and its alloys on an industrial scale would have wide applications, the only solutions available are those given in Table 18 for electropolishing on a laboratory scale. These solutions should be useful starting points for the development of techniques of electropolishing on an industrial scale.

9.7. NICKEL

Electropolishing of nickel on an industrial scale has been limited, since bright nickel plating can produce a comparable finish. However, the process could become of industrial importance as a finishing stage after semi-bright plating. Semi-bright plating solutions may be justified on the grounds that they are free from some of the drawbacks of the bright nickel solutions, e.g. high cost, great difficulty of control and brittleness of bright deposits.

The electropolishing process described by HOTHERSALL and HAMMOND [129] is a simple one with commercial possibilities. The conditions for polishing are:

Solution: 400 ml sulphuric acid
270 ml water
Cathode: Nickel
Voltage: 10–20
Current density: 15–33 A/dm² (140–300 A/ft²)

Time: 2–5 min
Temperature: 30°C (80°F)

The chief drawback of this solution is that it tends to become supersaturated with nickel sulphate, so that the excess salt precipitates and fouls the bath. An orthophosphoric acid–sulphuric acid bath has been developed for nickel and its alloys, including Monel metal, by the Battelle Memorial Institute [183]. The operating conditions are:

Solution: 13–15 wt. per cent sulphuric acid
               56–63 wt. per cent orthophosphoric acid
               2·5 wt. per cent trivalent aluminium
               1·4 wt. per cent trivalent chromium
               0·5–1·0 wt. per cent divalent nickel
               Remainder water
Cathode: Nickel
Voltage: 2·5
Current   5·4–54 A/dm² (50–500 A/ft², optimum 200
density: A/ft²)
Time: 10–20 min
Temperature: 30–105°C (80–220°F, optimum 115–130°F)

The condition of the bath is readily determined by measurements of specific gravity and acid ratio. Various modifications of this solution may be obtained by altering the acid ratio and by using additions of various metal ions but these are also covered by the patent. The preparation of such solutions is described fully in § 9.2.

9.8.   SILVER

The industrial electropolishing of silver and silver-plate has only developed rapidly in recent years although silver was one of the first metals to be electropolished commercially. In the cutlery industry the finishing costs have been reduced greatly by electropolishing.

The method developed for industrial application differs from the laboratory method in that the bath is stirred to give higher current densities and hence reduced polishing times [184, 185]. The stirring must be regulated since violent motion interferes with the voltage control; movement of the solution should provide a uniform flow over all parts of the anode. The operating conditions are:

Solution: 32·4 g silver added as potassium silver cyanide
19·5 g free potassium cyanide
41·5 g potassium carbonate
1000 ml water

Cathode: Stainless steel or silver

Voltage: Approx. 2·5

Current
density: 3·3 A/dm² (30 A/ft.²)

Time: 16–60

Temperature: 20°C (68°F)

Continuous processing is carried out by moving the rack steadily through the electrolyte at a rate of 50 to 100 cm/min (20 to 40 in./min). The rack should be kept away from the cathode and from the walls of the bath to prevent turbulence disturbing the polishing action. The optimum composition is quoted above, but good results can be obtained over a range of compositions. However, the operating voltage for each composition is critical and must be determined before polishing commences. If stainless steel cathodes are used, silver can be reclaimed by stripping.

A final polishing operation with rouge mops is sometimes necessary when streaks and faults in electrodeposited silver are revealed by electropolishing.

9.9. ZINC AND ZINC ALLOYS

Commercial electropolishing of zinc and zinc base die-castings is not yet practised, but the electropolishing of electrogalvanized wire and thin strip should be practicable and of commercial interest. The chromic acid–orthophosphoric acid electrolyte developed by the Battelle Memorial Institute [186] appears to be the most promising for industrial purposes.

CHAPTER 10

CHEMICAL POLISHING AND ITS
APPLICATION IN THE LABORATORY

10.1. RELATION BETWEEN ELECTROLYTIC AND
CHEMICAL POLISHING

IT IS well known that metal surfaces can be polished by immersion in a suitable solution *without* the application of an external potential and this process is called "chemical" polishing as distinct from "electrolytic" polishing. As in electropolishing, the results obtained vary from etching, where the surface may be smoothed but not brightened to "bright dipping," where the surface is brightened but not smoothed, depending on the solution and operating conditions.

Little experimental work has been done on the mechanism of chemical polishing, but the recorded observations show that there is a strong similarity between chemical polishing and electrolytic polishing (see, for example, the survey by PINNER [187]). As in the case of electropolishing, the functions of an ideal chemical polishing process are:

(a) smoothing of the surface irregularities;

(b) brightening without the appearance of etch pits.

During electropolishing these functions have been associated with two distinct processes, namely (i) the formation of a viscous layer around the anode, and (ii) the formation of a thin surface film. Consider these processes in the case of chemical polishing.

(i) *The formation of a viscous layer.*

Viscous layers of complexes have been observed on the metal during polishing. Little data is available on the nature of such layers but BEAUJARD [192] has suggested that the dense brown layer formed when iron is chemically polished in a nitric acid–hydrofluoric acid solution contains complexes with $FeNO^{3+}$ ions. These can decompose to form FeF_6^{3-} ions which are soluble in the solution. Under conditions where a viscous layer is observed, the rate is apparently controlled by diffusion in this layer since rotation of the specimen reduces the smoothing efficiency [2].

However, in many solutions, the rate of metal dissolution is so rapid or the rate of gas evolution is so vigorous that it is difficult to visualize the formation of a stable viscous layer. That diffusion is not the controlling process in these cases can be readily demonstrated by rotating a horizontal disk in the solution (see § 1.2.3) [29]. With increase in speed of rotation no marked zone of etching is observed at the outer edge as in the case of systems under diffusion control, where turbulence prevents the formation of a viscous layer. In fact, in some cases, the brilliance of finish is improved by increased speeds of rotation. Chemical polishing under these conditions appears to be equivalent to electropolishing at high current densities with vigorous gas evolution. TEGART and VINES [23] have suggested that in this case the viscous layer forms only in the valleys since at the peaks it is swept away by the turbulent flow. Marked preferential attack then occurs at the peaks leading to rapid smoothing (see the discussion to [15]).

(ii) *The formation of a surface film*

Although some early work [188] suggested that some type of surface film existed during chemical polishing, little direct evidence has yet been presented. The mercury drop technique used by HOAR and FARTHING [17] to demonstrate the presence of films during electropolishing has been applied by the author to chemical polishing [29]. In general, the results for a large number of metal/solution combinations indicate that the metals are covered with a surface film during chemical polishing. The nature of the films is not revealed by such experiments but they are probably either oxides or hydroxides because the solutions used in chemical polishing are strong oxidizing agents.

The reactions of nitric acid solutions with copper and copper alloys, particularly the brasses, have been discussed by PINNER [187] and SCHMID and SPAHN [189]. It is known that the rate of dissolution of copper in nitric acid is increased by traces of nitrous acid and it is suggested that dissolution is controlled by formation of an oxide film and its subsequent reduction by the nitrous acid. Some further evidence comes from the work of HICKLING and his co-workers [190] which indicates that a very thin film of oxide is formed during the polishing of iron in an oxalic acid–hydrogen peroxide solution. This film of ferric oxide is then attacked by the oxalic acid and an active state ⇌ partially passive state cycle is set up, leading to periodic potential variations similar to those observed in some cases of electropolishing.

The influence of such cycles on the brightening process may be demonstrated readily with aluminium by alternately anodizing a specimen and removing the film of alumina with acid. After several cycles the surface becomes quite bright [191].

As in the case of electropolishing (see § 1.2.4), the presence of a thin surface film provides an explanation for the absence of etch pits on polished surfaces.

10.2. LABORATORY METHODS FOR SPECIFIC METALS AND THEIR ALLOYS

Methods are now available for the chemical polishing of a large number of metals and their alloys in the laboratory and suitable methods are listed in the following tables. In general the rates of dissolution are much higher than for electropolishing and rough surfaces can be smoothed rapidly. In some cases, e.g. the routine examination of magnesium, lead and zinc and their alloys, electropolishing methods are not suitable and here chemical polishing provides a rapid and easy alternative to mechanical polishing.

For solutions containing fuming nitric acid, it is essential to wash the specimens extremely rapidly after removing them from the solution in order to prevent severe pitting.

Except where otherwise stated, the acids in the solutions are concentrated reagent grade acids of the following specific gravities:

orthophosphoric acid	(98 per cent)	sp. gr. 1·84
sulphuric acid	(98·08 per cent)	sp. gr. 1·84
nitric acid	(63·02 per cent)	sp. gr. 1·40
hydrochloric acid	(36·47 per cent)	sp. gr. 1·175
glacial acetic acid	(60·05 per cent)	sp. gr. 1·065

Table 28. Aluminium, Beryllium and Cadmium

Metal	Solution	Time	Temp. (°C)	Ref. No.	Remarks
Aluminium and alloys	25 ml sulphuric acid 70 ml orthophosphoric acid 5 ml nitric acid	30 sec– 2 min	85	193, 194	Very useful for studying alloys containing inter-metallic compounds, e.g. Al–Cu, Al–Fe and Al–Si alloys.
Beryllium	5 wt per cent sulphuric acid 75 wt per cent orthophosphoric acid 7 wt per cent chromic acid Remainder water	Several min	49–50	195	Rate of metal removal is approx. 1 micron/min. Passive film formed may be removed by immersion for 15 to 30 sec in 10 per cent sulphuric acid.
Cadmium	75 ml fuming nitric acid 25 ml water	5–10 sec	20	196	Cycles of dipping for a few seconds followed immediately by washing in a rapid stream of water are used until a bright surface is obtained. A suitable etching procedure uses 70 ml glacial acetic acid, 30 ml fuming nitric acid for 30 sec to 1 min. Can also be used for zinc.

Table 29. Copper and Germanium

Metal	Solution	Time	Temp. (°C)	Ref. No.	Remarks
Copper	33 ml nitric acid 33 ml orthophosphoric acid 33 ml glacial acetic acid	1–2 min	60–70	197	Finish is better when copper oxide is absent. A modified solution namely, 20 ml nitric acid, 55 ml orthophosphoric acid, 25 ml glacial acetic acid, appears to give a better polish than the original.
Copper alloys	30 ml nitric acid 10 ml hydrochloric acid 10 ml orthophosphoric acid 50 ml glacial acetic acid	1–2 min	70–80	197	Specimen should be agitated.
Copper–zinc alloys	80 ml fuming nitric acid 20 ml water	5 sec	40	196	Use periods of 5 sec immersion followed immediately by washing in a rapid stream of water. Slight variations in composition are needed for α–β and β–γ brasses to prevent differential attack. With β–γ alloys, a dull film forms and this can be removed by immersion in a saturated solution of chromic acid in fuming nitric acid for a few seconds followed by washing.
Germanium	15 ml hydrofluoric acid 25 ml nitric acid 15 ml glacial acetic acid 3–4 drops bromine	5–10 sec	20	198	

Table 30. Iron, Lead and Magnesium

Metal	Solution	Time	Temp. (°C)	Ref. No.	Remarks
Iron	3 ml nitric acid 7 ml hydrofluoric acid (comm.) 30 ml water	2–3 min	60–70	192	Dense brown viscous layer forms on surface; layer is soluble in solution. Low carbon steels can also be polished, but the cementite is attacked preferentially.
Irons and steels	80 ml distilled water 28 ml oxalic acid (100 g/l) 4 ml hydrogen peroxide (30 per cent)	15 min	35	201, 202	The solution must be prepared freshly before use. Careful washing is necessary before treatment. A microstructure is obtained similar to that produced by mechanical polishing, followed by etching with Nital.
Lead	20 ml hydrogen peroxide (30 per cent) 80 ml glacial acetic acid	Periods of 5–10 sec	20	199	McAFEE [196] recommends using alternate immersions in this solution and in a solution of 10 g molybdic acid and 140 ml ammonium hydroxide in 240 ml water to which 60 ml nitric acid is finally added.
Magnesium	75 ml fuming nitric acid 25 ml water	Periods of 3 sec	20	196, 200	The reaction reaches almost explosive violence after about a minute but if allowed to continue it ceases after several minutes leaving a polished surface ready for examination. Specimen should be washed immediately after removal from solution.

Table 31. Nickel, Silicon, Tantalum, Zinc and Zirconium

Metal	Solution	Time	Temp. (°C)	Ref. No.	Remarks
Nickel	30 ml nitric acid 10 ml sulphuric acid 10 ml orthophosphoric acid 50 ml glacial acetic acid	$\frac{1}{2}$–1 min	85–95	197	This solution gives a very good polish.
Silicon	20 ml nitric acid 5 ml hydrofluoric acid (comm.)	5–10 sec	20	198	
Tantalum	50 ml sulphuric acid 20 ml nitric acid 20 ml hydrofluoric acid (comm.)	5–10 sec	20	203	Solution is useful for preparing surfaces prior to anodizing.
Zinc	200 g chromic acid 15 g sodium sulphate 50 ml nitric acid 950 ml water	Several min to $\frac{1}{2}$ hr	20	214	Dense layer formed during treatment is soluble in water. Rate of dissolution is approximately 7 microns/min.
Zirconium	45 ml nitric acid 8–10 ml hydrofluoric acid (comm.) 45 ml water or hydrogen peroxide (30 per cent)	5–10 sec	20	204	Specimen is swabbed with solution. After a few seconds, a brownish-yellow vapour is evolved on the surface. Swabbing is continued for 5–10 sec and then specimen is rinsed in running water. Similar solution can be used for titanium and hafnium.

CHAPTER 11

INDUSTRIAL METHODS FOR THE CHEMICAL POLISHING OF SPECIFIC METALS AND THEIR ALLOYS

11.1. GENERAL PRINCIPLES

WHILE the industrial application of electropolishing has been retarded by the heavy capital outlay required for electrical equipment and the difficulty of adapting the process to the requirements of the production line, such factors do not apply to chemical polishing since the initial capital outlay is usually restricted to the tank itself. Any plating plant with efficient fume extraction can be adapted readily to the process. Among the metals which can be chemically polished on an industrial scale are aluminium and most wrought aluminium alloys, cadmium, copper and copper alloys, nickel and zinc. As yet ferrous alloys cannot be chemically polished on an industrial scale although the Marshall process [202] offers possibilities.

The tanks and fittings are normally constructed of stainless steel and equipment for controlling the temperature of the bath may be required. If gas bubbles are evolved at the metal surface during treatment mechanical agitation is necessary to prevent streaking. Efficient fume extraction is desirable particularly when nitric and acetic acid solutions are used at elevated temperatures. After treatment, chemically polished articles must be washed rapidly to prevent staining.

As with electropolishing, the best results are obtained on pure metals or single phase alloys, since inclusions and particles of a second phase give rise to problems similar to those discussed in § 4.3. As a general rule, the degree of smoothing obtained varies inversely with the grain size of the metal.

Many of the solutions used for chemical polishing of metals in the laboratory are not suitable for use on an industrial scale. Less concentrated solutions are generally used so that the rate of dissolution of metal is decreased. Therefore, chemical polishing finds its widest application in industry as a finishing treatment. It is not suitable for precision machining since there is no way of controlling metal dissolution comparable to that used in electromachining (§ 8.2.2).

11.2. METHODS FOR SPECIFIC METALS AND THEIR ALLOYS

11.2.1.   Aluminium and aluminium alloys [173, 205]

The main industrial application of chemical polishing is the finishing of components before anodizing. Two types of finish can be obtained:

(a) A highly polished mirror finish is obtained by using solutions containing more than 70 vol. per cent of orthophosphoric acid. Such solutions are suitable for finishing surfaces which have been mechanically polished and give results comparable to the Brytal and Alzak electropolishing processes. The solutions operate under viscous layer conditions similar to those found with orthophosphoric acid solutions in electro-polishing. Aluminium of commercial purity as well as Al–Mg–Zn and Al–Cu–Mg alloys, containing not more than 8 per cent zinc and 4 per cent copper respectively, can be treated with such solutions.

(b) A bright finish is obtained by using solutions containing 40 to 65 vol. per cent orthophosphoric acid but the specular reflectivity is lower than that of a mechanically polished surface. These solutions operate with a marked evolution of gas. The finish is usually adequate for decorative anodizing, but the process is only suitable for aluminium of at least 99·5 per cent purity.

Most of the solutions used for aluminium and its alloys are based on orthophosphoric acid to which nitric, sulphuric or acetic acids are added. A typical orthophosphoric acid–nitric acid solution giving a type (a) finish is:

Solution:	805 ml orthophosphoric acid
	35 ml nitric acid
	160 ml water
Time:	$\frac{1}{4}$–5 min depending on initial surface
Temperature:	Approximately 80°C

The addition of acetic acid improves the finish and although many different compositions are in use, a typical solution is:

Solution: 700 ml orthophosphoric acid (sp. gr. 1·50)
              30 ml nitric acid
              120 ml glacial acetic acid
              150 ml water
Time: 2–6 min
Temperature: 100–120°C

The life of these solutions depends on the build-up of aluminium in the solution, since the finish deteriorates when the aluminium content of the solution exceeds 20 to 30 g/l. However, the replacement of solution lost by "dragout" and volatilization often counterbalances the build-up of aluminium, leading to a reasonably long working life. The minimum tank capacity recommended for economic use is 160 l. (50 gal).

A whole range of orthophosphoric–sulphuric–nitric acid solutions is used in practice and examples are listed in Table 32 [193]. These solutions have proved very satisfactory for polishing Brillalumag 3 and Alumag 50 (alloys developed especially for their electropolishing properties) [166].

An interesting development is the use of dilute solutions containing hydrofluoric acid or fluorides and oxidizing agents, particularly

Table 32. *Compositions of Solutions used for Chemical Polishing of Aluminium* [193]

Type	Orthophosphoric acid (sp. gr. 1·71)	Sulphuric acid (sp. gr. 1·84)	Nitric acid (sp. gr. 1·50)	Temp. (°C)
a	300	600	70–100	115–120
a	400	500	60–100	100–120
a	500	400	60–100	95–115
a	600	300	50–80	95–115
b	700	250	30–80	85–110
b	800	100	30–80	85–110
b	900	50	30–80	85–105

nitric acid. These solutions can give very good results on super purity aluminium, but are not suitable for lower purities. The details of the "Erftwerk" process used in Germany are [206]:

Solution: 100–170 (preferably 130) g nitric acid
               100–200 (preferably 160) g ammonium
                                          bifluoride
               0·08–0·8 (preferably 0·2) g lead
                                          nitrate
                          1000   ml   water
Time: 15–30 sec
Temperature: 50–80°C.

The life of such solutions depends on the exhaustion of the ammonium bifluoride, but care must be taken in replenishing this since commercial grade ammonium bifluoride contains small quantities of lead and these can build up to an excessive lead content in the solution with consequent deterioration in finish. A polythene-lined tank may be used but the operating temperature must not exceed 60°C and adequate cooling is necessary for continuous usage.

On removal from the solution, the metal surface is very reactive and the article must be rinsed rapidly in water and then in 40 to 50 per cent nitric acid to passivate the surface. If anodizing is not carried out immediately, the article must be stored in a 1 per cent potassium dichromate or chromic acid solution to prevent the formation of a porous, non-adherent oxide film. About 8 microns of metal is removed during the treatment.

11.2.2.   Cadmium

It is possible to obtain a smooth bright surface on cadmium plate by chemical polishing. Two main types of solutions are in use:

(a) *chromic–sulphuric acid solutions* [207]:

Solution: A   B
               100   150 g chromic acid
               1·67   3·75 g sulphuric acid
               1000   1000 ml water

Time: 2–30 sec
Temperature: 20–30°C

Some variation in composition is permissible but, if the ratio CrO_3/SO_4 falls below 20, a yellow film, insoluble in water, is formed on the cadmium. Similar films are formed when the concentration of trivalent chromium exceeds 10 g/l. In both cases the film can be removed by rinsing in a dilute solution of approximately 2 per cent sulphuric acid. About 1 to 10 microns of metal is removed during treatment and it is necessary to ensure that a sufficient thickness of cadmium has been electrodeposited particularly in recesses and angles.

(b) *hydrogen peroxide solutions* [208]

Solution: 70 ml hydrogen peroxide (30 per cent)
3 ml sulphuric acid
927 ml water
Time: 15–20 sec
Temperature: 20–30°C.

If the solution contains too much acid, a white finish is obtained; if too much hydrogen peroxide is present, the brightening is quicker but the solution is unstable. Sulphuric acid may be replaced by other acids, e.g. hydrochloric, acetic or lactic acid. The solution should be stored in glass or stainless steel tanks. In order to avoid contamination, the articles to be polished should be given a pre-treatment in 1 per cent sulphuric acid and then rinsed in water. This solution is cheaper to prepare and maintain than the chromate type solutions. However, the brilliance and corrosion resistance of the polished surface are not as good as with the chromate solutions.

11.2.3. Copper and copper alloys [209]

The Battelle Memorial Institute [210] has developed a process based on a mixture of nitric, orthophosphoric and acetic acids for the chemical polishing of copper and its alloys. The composition varies with the metal to be treated within the following limits:

30–80 vol. per cent orthophosphoric acid
5–20 vol. per cent nitric acid
10–50 vol. per cent glacial acetic acid
0–10 vol. per cent water.

A typical process for copper and α-brass is:

Solution: 550 ml orthophosphoric acid
              200 ml nitric acid
              250 ml glacial acetic acid
              5 ml hydrochloric acid
Time: 2–6 min
Temperature: 55–80°C.

SCHMID and SPAHN [211] have carried out an extensive investigation of the polishing of brass and nickel–silver in various solutions at various temperatures. They used a standard treatment time of 5 min and examined the resultant surfaces with a reflectometer to obtain a quantitative assessment of the polish. Their results show that the composition of the solution is not particularly critical for brasses, but is critical for nickel–silver (60 per cent copper, 18 per cent nickel, 22 per cent zinc).

These solutions have several disadvantages, viz. high cost, short life due to rapid build-up of metal in the solution and difficulty of control. SCHMID and SPAHN have investigated aqueous solutions of nitric and orthophosphoric acids and obtained promising results with solutions of 60 vol. per cent orthophosphoric acid, 30 vol. per cent water and 10 vol. per cent nitric acid. However, the smoothing action is not as efficient as with solutions containing acetic acid.

PINNER [209] reports the development of a process based on a dilute solution consisting of orthophosphoric acid, nitric acid and hydrochloric acid operating at 25 to 35°C. However, no details of the solution are yet available.

11.2.4. Ferrous alloys

There is no solution suitable for the chemical polishing of ferrous alloys on a large scale. However, a process has been used for specialized applications such as pre-treatment for heavy nickel plating, precision finishing of heat-treated gears and the preparation of smooth surfaces on gauges [202]. This process is slow (about

0·2 micron/min for mild steel) and the solution is unstable and deteriorates rapidly with use.

The best results are obtained with the following conditions:

Solution: 25 g oxalic acid (crystals)
               13 g hydrogen peroxide (30 per cent)
               0·1 g sulphuric acid
               1000 ml water
Time: 30–60 min depending on initial finish
Temperature: 20–30°C.

Higher temperatures and agitation of the solution both reduce the time of treatment, but impair the quality of the finish. If the concentration of the solution is increased, the quality of the finish is unaffected but the stability of the solution decreases. On immersion, copious evolution of gas occurs but this becomes intermittent after some time.

The best results are obtained with mild steel and white heart malleable cast iron. High carbon and alloy steels are not suitable since they become coated with passivating films.

11.2.5. Nickel

Nickel may be polished in solutions of the orthophosphoric-nitric–acetic acid type used for copper, but due to the high rate of dissolution of the metal the process is not suitable for polishing dull nickel plate of normal thickness. It is not competitive in quality or cost with bright nickel plating or electropolishing.

11.2.6. Zinc

The processes outlined for cadmium can also be used for zinc plated parts and to some extent for diecastings.

APPENDIX I

RATES OF ANODIC DISSOLUTION

A KNOWLEDGE of the rate of anodic dissolution is useful when it is necessary to remove known thicknesses of metal under controlled conditions. Unless gas is evolved at the anode, the rate of dissolution conforms to Faraday's Law. Metals usually dissolve with their normal chemical valency, except in perchloric acid solutions, where some metals appear to dissolve with the abnormal valencies shown in Table 33 [212]. The abnormal values are attributed to the metal dissolving in several valency states, the ratios of the amounts dissolved giving rise to the fractional values. With aluminium, for example, it is postulated that an unstable monovalent ion can occur and thus Al^+ and Al^{3+} ions are present in solution. The apparent valency of 1·3 then indicates that 85 per cent of the ions are Al^+. Table 32 shows that only fairly reactive metals have abnormal valencies and STRAUMANIS [213] suggests that simultaneous chemical and electrolytic dissolution of the metal takes place, leading to a weight loss greater than that expected for ions of normal valency.

The available data for rates of anodic dissolution in typical electrolytes is given in Table 34.

Table 33. *Valencies of Metals in Perchloric Acid Solutions*

Metal	Usual valency	Observed valency	Metal	Usual valency	Observed valency
Ag	1	1·0	Mo	3, 6	3·0
Hg	1, 2	1·0	Zr	2, 4	2·0
Pb	2, 4	2·0	Zn	2	1·4
Bi	3, 5	3·0	U	3, 4, 6, 8	1·4
Sn	2, 4	2·0	Mn	2, 3, 4, 6, 7	1·7
Ni	2	2·0	V	2, 5	2·0
Co	2, 3	2·0	Al	3	1·3
In	1, 2, 3	1·0	Be	2	1·0
Cd	2	2·0	Ti	2, 4	1·5
Fe	2, 3	2·0	Mg	2	1·2
Ga	1, 2, 3	1·0			

Table 34. *Typical Rates of Anodic Dissolution*

Metal	Electrolyte	Polishing condition	Rate (microns per min)	Ref.
Aluminium	Perchloric acid–acetic anhydride	7 A/dm²	3	107
Copper	1000 g/l orthophosphoric acid	4 A/dm²	0·9	95
Copper–lead alloy (73% Cu, 27% Pb)	Orthophosphoric acid– ethyl alcohol	1·85–1·9 V 1 A/dm²	2	95
Leaded bronzes	Orthophosphoric acid– ethyl alcohol	4·5–5·0 V 9–10 A/dm²	4	95
Iron (Armco)	Perchloric acid–acetic anhydride solution high in dissolved iron		1·0	95
Carbon steel	Perchloric acid–acetic anhydride	4–10 A/dm²	0·7–0·8	39, 58
18/8 steel	Perchloric acid–acetic anhydride		0·6	95
18/8 steel	Orthophosphoric acid– glycerine	1·6 A/dm²	0·15	95
Magnesium	Orthophosphoric acid– ethyl alcohol	0·5 A/dm²	0·25	107
Nickel	Perchloric acid–acetic anhydride	40 A/dm²	6	95
Tin	Perchloric acid–acetic anhydride	10 A/dm²	5	95
Tin	Evans and Whitwham's solution	25 V 30 A/dm²	30	138
Tin	Perchloric acid		420	100
Titanium	Perchloric acid–acetic anhydride	20–30 A/dm²	12	99
Uranium	Perchloric acid–acetic acid	5 A/dm²	1·9	102
Zinc	Orthophosphoric acid– alcohol solution high in dissolved zinc	0·5 A/dm²	0·2	95

APPENDIX II

AMOUNT OF METAL REMOVED BY MECHANICAL AND ELECTROLYTIC POLISHING

THE data in Table 35 were obtained by MERCHANT [59] during the metallographic preparation of steel specimens by mechanical and electrolytic polishing techniques. The total amount of metal removed during a single preparation is approximately the same for both methods. However, with mechanical polishing, it is often necessary to polish and etch several times to ensure that all traces of disturbed metal have been removed, whereas, with electrolytic polishing, one treatment is usually sufficient.

(Table 35 opposite)

Table 35.

Mechanical Polishing

Procedure	Average thickness removed in procedure (microns)
Grinding on "0" emery paper	8
Grinding on "00" emery paper	6
Grinding on "000" emery paper	4
Grinding on "0000" emery paper	3
Polishing on rotating wheel with chromic oxide and water	1·5
15 sec etch in 2 per cent Nital	0·5
Total	23

Electrolytic Polishing

Procedure	Average thickness removed in procedure (microns)
Grinding on "0" emery paper	8
Grinding on "00" emery paper	6
Grinding on "000" emery paper	4
Electrolytic polishing with perchloric acid solution (98) under optimum conditions (4 A/dm², 8 min polishing time)	6
5 sec etch in 2 per cent Nital	0·1
Total	24·1

APPENDIX III

ANALYSIS OF SULPHURIC ACID–ORTHOPHOSPHORIC ACID ELECTROPOLISHING SOLUTIONS

UNDER industrial conditions where large areas of metal are treated, close control of the acid contents of the electropolishing solutions is necessary to ensure optimum finish. Many industrial electropolishing solutions use mixtures of sulphuric and orthophosphoric acids. For such mixtures, a simple rapid method of analysis has been developed [214]. This method is based on the facts that, in titrating the acid solutions with standard sodium hydroxide to the methyl orange end-point, the whole of the sulphuric acid and one-third of the orthophosphoric acid is neutralized, whereas if the titration is made to the phenolphthalein end-point, then all the sulphuric acid and two-thirds of the orthophosphoric acid will be neutralised. From the two titrations the concentrations of the sulphuric acid and of the orthophosphoric acid can be calculated.

Reagents required

Methyl orange solution: 0·1 g of methyl orange is dissolved in 100 ml of hot water and filtered if necessary.

Phenolphthalein solution: 0·1 g of phenolphthalein is dissolved in 100 ml of a solution of equal parts of water and ethyl alcohol.

Standard sodium hydroxide solution N/10; 4·000 g of pure sodium hydroxide is dissolved in 1000 ml of water and the solution standardized against potassium acid phthalate.

Procedure

(1) Take 5 ml of the electropolishing solution by pipette, transfer to a 500 ml standard flask and dilute to the mark with water.

(2) Take a 10 ml aliquot, transfer to a 250 ml Erlenmeyer flask and dilute with 150 ml water.

(3) Add 4 drops of methyl orange solution.

(4) Titrate with N/10 sodium hydroxide solution to the methyl orange end-point.

(5) Add 4 drops of phenolphthalein solution and continue the titration to the phenolphthalein end-point.

114

Calculations

Let A = the volume of sodium hydroxide required to give the methyl orange end-point,

and let B = the volume of sodium hydroxide required to give the phenolphthalein end-point.

Then $(2A - B) \times 2\cdot78$ = vol. per cent sulphuric acid (sp. gr. 1·84) and $(B - A) \times 6\cdot22$ = vol. per cent orthophosphoric acid (sp. gr. 1·75).

If the solution contains only orthophosphoric acid then $A \times 6\cdot23$ = vol. per cent orthophosphoric acid (sp. gr. 1·75).

REFERENCES

1. EVANS, U. R. Metallic Corrosion, Passivity and Protection, 2nd ed., Edward Arnold, London (1948).

2. EDWARDS, J. An Experimental Study of Electropolishing, *J. Electrodep. Tech. Soc.* **28** (1952) 133.

3. EDWARDS, J. The Mechanism of Electropolishing of Copper in Phosphoric Acid Solutions. I. Processes Preceding the Establishment of Polishing Conditions; II. Mechanism of Smoothing, *J. Electrochem. Soc.* **100** (1953) 189C and 223C.

4. EPELBOIN, I. Heavy Reduction Electrolytic Thinning and its Applications, (in French), *Rev. Met.* **49** (1952) 863.

5. KORTÜM, G. and BOCKRIS, J. O'M. *Textbook of Electrochemistry*, Vol. II. Elsevier, Amsterdam (1951).

6. JACQUET, P. A. The Mechanism of Electrolytic Polishing of Copper, (in French), *C. R. Acad. Sci. (Paris)* **202** (1936) 402.

On the Electrolytic Polishing of Copper, Lead, Tin and their Alloys and its Application to Metallography, (in French), *Bull. Soc. Chim. franc.* **3** (1936) 705.

7. ELMORE, W. C. Electrolytic Polishing, *J. App. Phys.* **10** (1939) 724.

8. HONEYCOMBE, R. W. K., and HUGHAN, R. R. Electrolytic Polishing of Copper in Orthophosphoric Acid, *J. Council Sci. Ind. Res. (Aust.)* **20** (1947) 297.

9. WALTON, H. F. The Anode Layer in the Electrolytic Polishing of Copper, *J. Electrochem. Soc.* **97** (1950) 219.

BATASHEV, K. P. and NIKITIN, E. N. Anodic Processes During Electrolytic Polishing of Copper in Orthophosphoric Acid, (in Russian), *Zhur. Priklad. Khim.* **23** (1950) 263.

10. DE SY, A. and
HAEMERS, H.

The Principles and Applications of Electrolytic Polishing in Metallography, (in French), *A.I.Lg. Congres., Section Met., Sous-Section Met. Physique* (1947) 193.

11. HICKLING, A. and
HIGGINS, J. K.

The Rate-Determining Stage in the Anodic Dissolution of Metals, *Trans. Inst. Met. Finishing* **29** (1953) 274.

12. ZEMBURA, Z. and
MICHALIK, W.

The Limiting Current During Electrolytic Polishing of Copper in a 20 N H_3PO_4 Solution, (in English), *Bull. Acad. Pol. Sci.* Cl III **5** (1957) 1073.

13. JACQUET, P. A.

Electrolytic Polishing of Metallic Surfaces. Part I, *Metal Finishing* **47** (5) (1949) 48.

14. LAFORGUE-KANTZNER,
D.

On the Electrolysis of Phosphoric Acid between Copper Electrodes: Electrolytic Polishing, (in French), *C. R. Acad. Sci.* (*Paris*) **233** (1951) 547.

15. WAGNER, C.

Contribution to the Theory of Electropolishing, *J. Electrochem. Soc.* **101** (1954) 225; see discussion by NICHOLAS, J. F. and TEGART, W. J. McG. ibid **102** (1955) 93C.

16. PIONTELLI, R.

Contribution to the Knowledge of the Process of Electrolytic Polishing. Note II, (in Italian), *Met. Ital.* **12** (1950) 205.

PIONTELLI, R. and
BIANCHI, G.

Contribution to the Knowledge of the Process of Electrolytic Polishing of Metals III, (in French), *Comptes Rendues de III Reunion, Comité Int. de Thermo-dynamique et de Cin. Electrochim.* (*Berne*) (1951) 161.

17. HOAR, T. P. and
FARTHING, T. W.

Solid Films on Electropolishing Anodes, *Nature* **169** (1952) 324.

18. MEUNIER, L.

On the Dynamic Functioning of a Cell for the Electrolytic Polishing of Copper, (in French), *Comptes Rendues de II Reunion, Comité Int. de Thermo-dynamique et de Cin. Electrochim.* (*Milan*) (1950) 242.

19. FRANCIS, H. T. and
COLNER, W. H.

Cyclic Phenomena Observed in the Electropolishing of Silver, *J. Electrochem. Soc.* **97** (1950) 237.

CHALIN, C. — On the Study of Periodic Oscillations Obtained During the Anodic Solution of Silver, (in French), *C. R. Acad. Sci.* (*Paris*) **233** (1951) 362.

20. HOAR, T. P. and MOWAT, J. A. S. — Mechanism of Electropolishing, *Nature* **165** (1950) 64.

21. FELIU, S. and SERRA, M. — The Mechanism of Electrolytic Polishing, *Comptes Rendues de VI Reunion, Comité Int. de Thermodynamique et de Cin. Electrochim.* (Poitiers) (1954) 483.

22. LAL, H. — The Nature of the Electropolishing State, *Symposium on Electroplating and Metal Finishing*, (Nat. Met. Lab. India) (1952), 54.

23. TEGART, W. J. McG. and VINES, R. G. — The Mechanism of Electrolytic Polishing of Metals, (in French), *Rev. Met.* **48** (1951) 245.
On the Mechanism of Electrolytic Polishing of Metals, *Trans. Aust. Inst. Metals* **5** (1952) 107.

24. CASEY, E. J. and BERGERON, R. E. — The Electrolytic Polishing of Amphoteric Metals, *Can. J. Chem.* **31** (1953) 422.

25. TEGART, W. J. McG. and VINES, R. G. — Unpublished work.

26. HOAR, T. P. and MOWAT, J. A. S. — The Electropolishing of Nickel in Urea-Ammonium Chloride Melts, *J. Electrodep. Tech. Soc.* **26** (1950) 7.

27. ROWLAND, P. R. — Mechanism of Electropolishing, *Nature* **171** (1953) 931.

28. BROUILLET, P. and EPELBOIN, I. — Two New Results Relative to the Composition of Electrolytic Polishing Baths, (in French), *Rev. Met.* **51** (1954) 693.

BROUILLET, P. — Contribution to the Study of Electrolysis in Very Concentrated Solutions. Example of Electrolytic Polishing, (in French), *Mét. Corr. Ind.* **30** (1955) 141, 192 and 343.

29. TEGART, W. J. McG. — Unpublished work.

30. TERMAN, F. E. — *Radio Engineers' Handbook*, McGraw-Hill, New York (1953) 198.

31. VERNON, W. H. J. and STROUD, E. G. — Electrolytic 'Polishing' of Zinc, *Nature* **142** (1938) 1161.

32. BATES, L. F. and MEE, C. D. — A Bridge Method for the Control of Electrolytic Polishing, *J. Sci. Instrum.* **27** (1950) 317.

33. EPELBOIN, I. On the Application of Thyratrons to the Electrolytic Polishing of Magnetic Materials, (in French), *Bull. Soc. franc. Electriciens* **9** (1949) 91.

34. EPELBOIN, I. On an Experimental Study of Electrolytic Polishing, (in French), *J. Chim. Phys.* **49** (1952) C 214.

35. EPELBOIN, I. A Process for Studying and Regulating
    CHALIN, C. and Electrolytic Polishing of Metals, (in
    GALPERIN, B. French), *Rev. Met.* **46** (1949) 151.

36. BERTEIN, F. Rapid Determination of Conditions for Electrolytic Polishing of Metal, (in French), *Met. et. Corr.* **21** (1946) 40.

37. LORKING, K. F. A Method for the Investigation of Electropolishing Problems, Dept. of Supply (Aust.), A.R.L. Report SM171 (1951); *Trans. Aust. Inst. Met.* **5** (1952) 109.

38. LORKING, K. F. The Influence of a Surface Active Agent on the Electropolishing of Copper, Dept. of Supply (Aust.), *A.R.L. Report* SM221 (1953).

39. MICHEL, P. Recent Research in Electrolytic Polishing, *Sheet. Met. Ind.* **26** (1949) 2175.

40. JACQUET, P. A. The Electrolytic Polishing of Metallic Surfaces. Part II, *Met. Finishing* **47** (6) (1949) 83; *see also*
    KNUTH-WINTERFELDT, Contribution to the Theory of Electrolytic
    E. Polishing, (in German), *Arch. f. Eisenhuttenwesen* **7/8** (1954) 393.

41. VON HAMOS, L. The Electrolytic Polishing of Metals for Microscopic Examination, (in Swedish), *Jernkontorets Annal.* **126** (1942) 568.

42. JACQUET, P. A. A Source of Error in Tracing the Current-Voltage Curve of Electrolytes in Anodic Polishing and its Application to the Study of Polishing, (in French), *C. R. Acad. Sci. (Paris)* **227** (1948) 556.

43. AGAR, J. N. and The Influence of Change of Size in
    HOAR, T. P. Electrochemical Systems, *Faraday Soc. Discuss. "Electrode Processes"* (1947) 158.

44. RAETHER, H. The Structure of Mechanically and Electrolytically Polished Surfaces, (in German), *Mikroscopie* **5** (1950) 101.

120   REFERENCES

45. JACQUET, P. A.   The Electrolytic Polishing of Metallic
                           Surfaces. Part III, *Met. Finishing* **47**
                           (7) (1949) 58.
                           Electrolytic and Chemical Polishing, *Met.
                           Reviews* **1** (1956) 157.

46. MOORE, A. J. W.   The Physical and Chemical Changes
                           which Accompany the Polishing of
                           Metals, *J. Electrodep. Tech. Soc.* **28**
                           (1952) 117.

47. FINCH, G. I.   The Sliding Surface, *Proc. Phys. Soc.*
                           A **63** (1950) 785.

48. BOWDEN, F. P. and   *The Friction and Lubrication of Solids*,
    TABOR, D.   Oxford Univ. Press (1950) Chap. III.

49. COURTEL, R.   Contribution of the Method of Electron
                           Diffraction to the Study of the Beilby
                           Layer, (in French), *Met. et Corr.* **22**
                           (1947) 157. *See, however,*

    SAMUELS, L. E. and   The Nature of Mechanically Polished
    SANDERS, J. V.   Surfaces;   An   Electron-Diffraction
                           Examination of Polished Silver Sur-
                           faces, *J. Inst. Metals* **87** (1958–59) 129.

50. MOORE, A. J. W. and   Rupture of Oxide Films During Repeated
    TEGART, W. J. McG.   Sliding, *Aust. J. Sci. Res.* A **4** (1951)
                           181; also *Proc. Roy. Soc.* A **212** (1952)
                           458.

51. SAMUELS, L. E.   The Nature of Mechanically Polished
                           Metal Surfaces: The Surface Deforma-
                           tion Produced by the Abrasion and
                           Polishing of 70 : 30 Brass, *J. Inst.
                           Metals* **85** (1956–57) 51.

    SAMUELS, L. E. and   The Nature of Mechanically Polished
    WALLWORK, G. R.   Metal Surfaces: Deformation Produced
                           During   Abrasion   of   18/8   Type
                           Austenitic Steel, *J. Iron & Steel Inst.*
                           186 (1957) 211.
                           The Nature of Mechanically Polished
                           Metal Surfaces: The Surface Deforma-
                           tion Produced During the Abrasion and
                           Polishing of Zinc, *J. Inst. Metals* **86**
                           (1957–58) 43.

52. JACQUET, P. A.   Contribution to the Experimental Study
                           of the Structure of Electrodeposits,
                           (in French), *Rev. Met.* **35** (1938) 41,
                           116, 176.

53. JACQUET, P. A. and JEAN, M. — Study of the Presence of and Importance of the Chemical Nature of Electrolytically Polished Metal Surfaces, (in French), *Rev. Met.* **48** (1951) 537.

54. ALLEN, J. A. — Oxide Films on Electrolytically Polished Copper Surfaces, *Trans. Faraday Soc.* **48** (1952) 273.

55. MADDIN, R. — Anomalies in the Appearance of Glide Ellipses, *Met. Tech.* (Feb. 1948) T.P. 2332.

56. WILMS, G. — Note on the Use of Electropolishing in the Metallographic Study of Plastic Deformation, *J. Inst. Metals* **76** (1950) 629.

57. WILSDORF, H. — The Electron-Microscopic Examination of Metal Surfaces with the Aid of Evaporated Silica Replicas, (in German), *Z. Metallkunde* **45** (1954) 14.

58. JACQUET, P. A. — Application of Interferential Contrast to the Study of Electrolytically Polished Surfaces, (in French), *Rev. Mét.* **54** (1957) 663.

59. MERCHANT, H. J. — The Application of Electrolytic Polishing to Ferrous Metallography, *J. Iron and Steel Inst.* **155** (1947) 179.

60. BUCKNELL, G. L., GEACH, G. A. and WELSH, N. C. — Regular Structures Produced on Aluminium by Electropolishing, *Research* **5** (1952) 289.

WELSH, N. C. — Pseudo-Subgrain Structures on Aluminium Surfaces, *J. Inst. Metals* **85** (1956–57) 129.

NISHIYAMA, Z., FUJITA, H. and KORE-EDA, A. — Electron-Microscopically Fine Patterns on the Electropolished Surface of Aluminium, *Mem. Inst. Sci. Ind. Res.* **14** (1957) 121.

61 JACQUET, P. A. — The Principles and Scientific Applications of the Electrolytic Polishing of Metals, *Electrodep. Tech. Soc. 3rd. Int. Conf. on Electrodeposition* (Sept. 1947), Paper No. 1.

The Electrolytic Polishing of Metallic Surfaces. Parts III, IV, V and VI, *Met. Finishing* **47** (7) (1949) 58; **47** (9) (1949) 60; **47** (10) (1949) 68; and **48** (2) (1950) 55.

62. SAMUELS, L. E.   The Use of Diamond Abrasives for a
                            Universal System of Metallographic
                            Polishing, *J. Inst. Metals* **81** (1953) 471;
                            see also *Metallurgia* **50** (1954) 303.

63. SCHOFIELD, T. H. and   The Microstructure of Wrought Non-
    CUCKOW, F. W.   Arsenical Phosphorus-Deoxidised Cop-
                            per Containing Small Amounts of
                            Bismuth, *J. Inst. Metals* **47** (1947)
                            377.

64. GAYLER, M. L.   Phenomena Observed after the Heat
                            Treatment of Electrolytically Polished
                            Aluminium—4 per cent Copper Alloy,
                            (in French), *Comptes Rendues Journees
                            des Etats de Surface* (*Paris*) (1945) 82.

65. JACQUET, P. A.   A Very Sensitive Micrographic Etch for
                            Copper, (in French), *C. R. Acad. Sci.*
                            (*Paris*) **218** (1944) 790.

66. LACOMBE, P.,   The True Physico-Chemical Properties of
    MORIZE, P. and   Metal Surfaces as Revealed by Electro-
    CHAUDRON, G.   lytic Polishing, (in French), *Rev. Met.*
                            44 (1947) 87.

67. CAPDECOMME, L.   The Reflecting Power of Copper, (in
                            French), *C. R. Acad. Sci.* (*Paris*) **204**
                            (1937) 1415.

68. WHITEHEAD, J. R.   Surface Deformation and Friction of
                            Metals at Light Loads, *Proc. Roy. Soc.*
                            A **201** (1950) 109.

69. MOUFLARD, M.   Critical Study of Measurement of Hard-
                            ness and Micro-hardness, (in French),
                            Met. et Corr. **23** (1948) 245.

70. BROWN, A. F. and   Microslip in Metal Crystals, *Phil. Mag.*
    HONEYCOMBE,   **42** (1951) 1142.
    R. W. K.

71. BROWN, A. F.   Surface Effects in Plastic Deformation of
                            Crystals, *Advanc. Phys.* **1** (1952) 427.

72. HAINES, H. R. and   The Production of Fine Wires by Electro-
    MOTT, B. W.   lytic Polishing, *J. Sci. Instrum.* **30** (1953)
                            459.

73. KORBELAK, A. and   Servo-Control in the Electropolishing of
    RIVELY, C. M.   Wire and Strip, *Plating* **41** (1954) 1446.

74. COLNER, W. H.,   Preparation of Very Fine Wire by
    FEINLEIB, M. and   Electropolishing, *Met. Prog.* **59** (1951)
    FRANCIS, H. T.   795.

75. NICHOLSON, R. E., THOMAS, G. and NUTTING, J.

A Technique for Obtaining Thin Foils of Aluminium and Aluminium Alloys for Transmission Electron Microscopy, *Brit. J. Appl. Phys.* **9** (1958) 25.

BOLLMANN, W.

Interference Effects in the Electron Microscopy of Thin Crystal Foils, *Phys. Rev.* **103** (1956) 1588.

TOMLINSON, H. W.

An Electro-Polishing Technique for the Preparation of Metal Specimens for Transmission Electron Microscopy, *Phil. Mag.* **3** (viii) (1958) 867.

76. TILEY, J. W. and WILLIAMS, R. A.

The Surface Barrier Transistor, II. Electrochemical Techniques for Fabrication of Surface Barrier Transistors, *Proc. Inst. Radio Eng.* **41** (1953) 1706.

77. STEINER, J.

Electropolishing with Rectified Current, (in German), *Metalloberfläche* **B6** (1954) 65.

78. POW, J.

Electrolytic Polishing of Iron and Steel, *Metal Treatment* **16** (1949) 31.

79. HANCHER, R. L.

An Improved Method for Routine Electrolytic Polishing of Microspecimens, *Metallurgia* **49** (1954), 47.

80. SYKES, E. C., HADDRELL, V. J., HAINES, H. R. and MOTT, B. W.

An Apparatus for Electropolishing Specimens for Metallographic Examination, *J. Inst. Metals* **83** (1954–55) 166.

81. Anon.

Exhibits of Metallurgical Interest at the Physical Society Exhibition, *Metallurgia* **50** (1954) 100; see also *The Engineer* **198** (1954) 880.

82. Anon.

Electropolisher, *Chem. and Eng. News* **24** (1946) 2399

83. Anon.

Cenco Electropolisher, *Rev. Sci. Instrum.* **17** (1946) 284.

84. Anon.

New Electrolytic Polisher Saves Time and Effort in Preparing Metal Specimens, *The Laboratory* **19** (5) 118.

85. Anon.

Electrolytic Polishing. New Equipment with Provision for Circulating the Electrolyte, *Metallurgia* **57** (1958) 107.

86. Anon.

New Apparatus for Rapid Production of Microspecimens, *Met. Ind.* **75** (Dec. 9) (1949) 493.

KNUTH-WINTERFELDT, E. — Micropol and Disa-Electropol—Two Quick Metallographic Polishers, *Trans. of Inst. and Measurements Conf.* Stockholm (1949) 223; *see also* Micropolishing, (in French), *Met. et Corr.* **23** (1948) 5.

87. DAMGAARD, L. G. and KNUTH-WINTERFELDT, E. — The Electrolysis Tube, a new Apparatus for Metallographic Methods, (in German), *Metalloberfläche* **11** (1957) 75.

88. JACQUET, P. A. — *Metallography of Aluminium and its Alloys. Use of Electrolytic Polishing*, (in French), Office National d'Études et de Recherches Aeronautiques, 25 Av. de la Div. Leclerc., Chatillon-sous-Bagneux (Paris) (1952).

89. MAZIA, J. — Electrolytic Polishing: Theory and Practice, *Monthly Rev. Am. Electroplaters' Soc.* **34** (1947) 937.

NAGAI, K. and MANO, K. — Electrolytic Slide-Polishing, *Sci. Rep. Res. Inst. Tohoku Univ.* B1/2 (1951) 391.

90. JACQUET, P. A. and VAN EFFENTERRE, A. — Non-Destructive Method for Macro- and Micrographic Surface Examination, (in French), *Rev. Met.* **54** (1957) 107.

JACQUET, P. A. — Rapid Method of Surface Preparation for Metallographic Examination. *Local Electrolytic Polishing*, (in French), *Note Tech.* No. 40, Office National d'Études et de Recherches Aeronautiques, 25, Av. de la Div. Leclerc, Chatillon-sous-Bagneux (Paris) (1957). Non-Destructive Techniques for Macro- and Micrographic Surface Examination of Metallic Specimens (Electrolytic Local Polishing and Replica Technique) *Proc. A.S.T.M.* **57** (1957) 1290. Improvements and New Applications of Non-Destructive Metallography, (in French), *Rev. Met.* **55** (1958) 531.

91. KEMSLEY, D. S. and TEGART, W. J. McG. — The Hazards in the Use of Perchloric Acid Electropolishing Solutions, *Phys. Met. Report* No. 8. (revised), Division of Tribophysics, CSIRO (1949). The section of this Report dealing with the use of non-explosive electrolytes for metallographic electropolishing was published in *Aust. Eng.* Nov. 8 (1948), 37.

92. JACQUET, P. A.

The Safe Use of Perchloric-Acetic Electro-polishing Baths, *Met. Finishing* **47** (11) (1949) 62.

93. JACQUET, P. A.

A New Technique for the Electrolytic Polishing of Aluminium and its Alloys, (in French), *Met. Corr. Usure* **18** (1943) 198.

94. HONEYCOMBE, R. W. K.

The Electrolytic Polishing and Etching of Metals, *Aust. Inst. Met. Symposium "Recent Advances in Phys. Met. Part* 1 *Metallography,"* (1944); *Aust. Eng. Year Book* (1944).

95. JACQUET, P. A.

Introduction to the Study and Use of Electrolytic Polishing of Metals and Alloys, (in French), *Met. Corr. Usure* **18** (1943) 1.

96. BLACK, G.

Electrolytic Polishing of Magnesium. I and II, *Met. Finishing* **45** (6) (1947) 86 and **45** (7) (1947) 84.

97. JACQUET, P. A. and FIGOUR, H.

Method for Machining Certain Metals to Give a Brilliant Surface, (in French), Fr. Pat. 707, 526 (1931).

98. JACQUET, P. A. and ROCQUET, P.

Application of Electrolytic Polishing to the Micrographic Examination of Iron and Steel, (in French), *C. R. Acad. Sci. (Paris)* **208** (1939) 1012.

99. JACQUET, P. A.

Electrolytic Polishing of Zirconium, Titanium and Beryllium, *Proc.* 1*st World Met. Cong.* (*Detroit*) (Oct. 1951) 732.

100. PUTTICK, K. E.

Electrolytic Polishing of Tin in Perchloric Acid, *Metallurgia* **14** (1949) 120.

101. JACQUET, P. A.

Improved Electrolytes for the Anodic Polishing of Certain Metals, *Sheet Met. Ind.* **26** (1949) 577; also *Rev. Met.* **49** (1949) 214.

102. JACQUET, P. A. and CAILLAT, R.

Electrolytic Polishing of Uranium for Physico-Chemical and Metallographic Study, (in French), *C. R. Acad. Sci. (Paris)* **228** (1949) 122.

103. PERRYMAN, E. C. W.

Recent Developments in Metallography, *Met. Ind.* **79** (2) (1951) 23.

104. MEDARD, L., JACQUET, P. A. and SARTORIUS, R.

On the Dangers of Explosion of Acetic-Perchloric Electrolytic Polishing Baths, (in French), *Rev. Met.* **46** (1949) 549.

MEDARD, L. and
SARTORIUS, R.

Experimental Study of the Explosive Properties of Acetic-Perchloric Mixtures, (in French), *Memorial des Poudres* **32** (1950) 179.

105. ELLIOTT, M. A. and
BROWN, F. W.

Report of Investigations of Explosion Hazards of Perchloric Acid and Organic Materials, *U.S. Bureau of Mines Rep. Inv.* 4169, (Jan. 1948).

106. DAWKINS, A. E.

Electrolytic Polishing [Hazards of CrO_3/ Acetic Acid Solution], *Met. Ind.* **88** Jan 27 (1956) 8; *J. Iron. & Steel Inst.* **82** (1956) 388.

107. JACQUET, P. A.

The Electrolytic Polishing of Metallic Surfaces and its Applications, Book I *"Aluminium, Magnesium, Light Alloys"*, (in French), Editions Métaux, 32 Rue de Marechal Joffre, Saint Germain-en-Laye, Paris (1948).

108. PLATEAU, J.,
WYON, G.,
PILLON, A. and
CRUSSARD, C.

Contribution to the Study of the Electrolytic Polishing of Aluminium, (in French), *Met. Corr. Usure* **26** (1951) 235.

109. DE SY, A. and
HAEMERS, H.

The Colouring of the Structural Constituents of Aluminium, (in German), *Aluminium* **24** (1942) 96.

110. LARKE, L. B. and
WICKS, E. H.

A Method for the Electrolytic Polishing and Etching of Some Al-Mg Alloys, Commercial Purity Aluminium and Pure Magnesium, *Metallurgia* **41** (1950) 172.

111. JACQUET, P. A.

Private communication.

112. MOTT, B. W. and
HAINES, H. R.

The Application of Polarized Light to the Examination of Various Anisotropic Metals and Intermetallic Phases, *J. Inst. Metals* **80** (1952) 629.

113. GWATHMEY, A. T.,
LEIDHEISER, H. and
SMITH, G. P.

Influence of Crystal Plane and Surrounding Atmosphere on Chemical Activities of Single Crystals of Metals, *N.A.C.A. Tech. Note* 1460 (1948).

114. ELMORE, W. C.

The Magnetic Structure of Cobalt, *Phys. Rev.* **53** (1938) 757.

115. PERRYMAN, E. C. W.

A New Solution for the Electrolytic Polishing of Copper and Copper-Base Alloys, Particularly Tin Bronzes, *Metallurgia* **46** (1952) 55.

116. JACQUET, P. A.   The Electrolytic Polishing of Lead Bronzes, Zinc and Magnesium, (in French), *Met. Corr. Usure* **19** (1944) 71.

117. A.S.T.M.   Electrolytic Polishing of Copper Alloys, Tentative Method E3–467 (1948); also *Metals Handbook* (1948) 901.

118. KUSHNER, J. B.   Modern Gold Plating, Part 27, *Products Finishing* **7** (1942) 42.

SCHUBIGER, R.   The Electrolytic Polishing of Gold and Dental Gold Alloys, (in German), Doctorate Thesis, Univ. Zurich (1958).

119. BAKISH, R. and ROBERTSON, W. D.   Metallographic Techniques for Cu-Au Alloys, *Trans. A.I.M.E.* **203** (1955) 424; *J. Metals* **7** (1955) 424.

120. ROTH, H. P.   Metallography of Hafnium, *Met. Prog.* **63** (6) (1953) 84.

121. GOSS, A. J. and VERNON, E. V.   The Growth and Orientation of Single Crystals of Indium, *Proc. Phys. Soc.* B **65** (1952) 905.

122. MORRIS, C. E.   Electropolishing of Steel in Chrome-Acetic Acid Electrolyte, *Met. Prog.* **56** (1949) 696.

123. DE DECKER, H. E. J., KRIJFF, A. P. and PLUUT, J. M.   Some Special Applications of Electropolishing, *Sheet Met. Ind.* **24** (1947) 2235.

124. MOULEN, A. W.   The Electrolytic Polishing of Lead-Tin Alloys for Microscopic Examination, *J. Electrochem. Soc.* **99** (1952) 133C.

125. JONES, E. and THIRSK, H. R.   Electrolytic Polishing of Lead in a Sodium Acetate-Acetic Acid Bath, *Nature* **171** (1953) 843.

126. COONS, W. C.   Simple Electrolytic Polishing Procedures for Molybdenum Metallographic Specimens, *Trans. A.S.M.* **41** (1949) 1415.
Fractographic and Metallographic Techniques for Molybdenum, *The Metal Molybdenum*, Am. Soc. Metals, Cleveland (1958) 394.

127. CHEN, N. K. and MADDIN, R.   Plasticity of Molybdenum Single Crystals, *Trans. A.I.M.E.* **191** (1951) 937; *J. Metals* **3** (1951) 937.

128. HOPKIN, G. L., JONES, J. E., MOSS, A. R. and PICKMAN, D. O.   The Arc Melting of Metals and its Application to the Casting of Molybdenum, *J. Inst. Metals* **82** (1954–55) 361.

129. HOTHERSALL, A. W.   The Anodic Polishing of Electrodeposited
and HAMMOND,   Nickel, *J. Electrodep. Tech. Soc.* **16**
R. A. F.   (1940) 83. The process is covered by
                       Br. Pat. 504,026 (1939).

130. WENSCH, G. W.   Electrolytic Polishing of Nickel, *Met.
Prog.* **58** (1950) 735.

131. MONTI, H.   Original Micrographic Methods for
Examination of Various Nuclear
Metals and Alloys, (in French), *Mét.
Corr. Ind.* **33** (1958) 481.

132. HESSELBERGER, W. M.   Electropolishing Silver, *Met. Ind.* **75**
(Aug. 26) (1949) 167.

133. SHUTTLEWORTH, R.,   A Note on the Electrolytic Polishing of
KING, R. and   Silver, *Met. Treatment* **14** (1947) 161.
CHALMERS, B.

134. MICHAEL, A. B. and   Observations on Etch-Pits and Sub-
HUEGEL, F. J.   Boundaries in Columbium (Niobium), *Acta Met.* **5** (1957) 339.

135. WENSCH, G. W.,   Polishing Tantalum, *Met. Prog.* **61** (1952)
BRUCKHART, K. B.   81. Tantalum has also been polished
and CONNOLY, M.   in hydrofluoric acid/nitric acid solution
(GALL and MILLER, Can. Pat. 435,261
(1947)) and in hydrofluoric acid/hydro-
chloric acid solution (WEI, Fr. Pat.
920,915 (1947)).

136. SMITH, M. D. and   The Sintering, Fabrication and Properties
HONEYCOMBE, R. W. K.   of Thorium, *J. Inst. Met.* **83** (1954) 421;
see also
ROTH, H. P.   Metallography of Thorium, *The Metal
Thorium*, Am. Soc. Metals, Cleveland
(1958) 282.

137. EVANS, U. R. and   Note on a Convenient Method of
WHITWHAM, D.   Electropolishing Aluminium Alloys,
J. Electrodep. Tech. Soc. **22** (1947) 24.

138. FENSHAM, P. J.   Self-Diffusion in Tin Crystals, *Aust. J.
Sci. Res.* A **3** (1950) 91; also private
communication.

139. SUTCLIFFE, D. A.,   Electrolytic Polishing of Titanium,
FORSYTH, J. I. M. and   *Metallurgia* **41** (1950) 283.
REYNOLDS, J. A.

140. OSADCHUK, R.,   Recommended Techniques for Polishing
KOSTER, W. P. and   Titanium for Metallographic Examina-
KAHLES, J. F.   tion, *Met. Prog.* **64** (4) (1953) 129.

141. HUGHES, J. M. and   Electropolishing of Tungsten, *Phys. Rev.*
COOMES, E. A.   **55** (1939) 1138; also **57** (1940) 1081.

142. MOTT, B. W. and   The Metallography of Uranium, *J. Inst.*
     HAINES, H. R.   *Metals* **80** (1952) 621.

143. ROBILLARD, A.,   Micrographic Examination of Uranium
     BOUCHER, R. and   by Formation of Epitaxial Layers by
     LACOMBE, P.   Atmospheric and Anodic Oxidation, (in
                             French), *Mét. Corr. Ind.* **31** (1956) 433.

144. KINZEL, A. B.   Vanadium Metal—a New Article of
                             Commerce, *Met. Prog.* **58** (1950) 315.
                             see also
     ROSTOKER, W.   *The Metallurgy of Vanadium*, John Wiley,
                             New York (1958) 140.

145. RODDA, J. L.   Electrolytic Polishing of Zinc and Brass,
                             Mining and Met. **24** (1943) 323.

146. RAMSAY, J. A.   Some Observations on the Deformation
                             of Polycrystalline Zinc, *J. Inst. Metals*
                             80 (1951) 167.

147. BRINSON, G.   Private communication.

148. BRINSON, G. and   The Study of Recrystallization in Zinc
     MOORE, A. J. W.   by Direct Observation, *J. Inst. Metals*
                             79 (1951) 429.

149. ROTH, H. P.   Metallography of Zirconium, *Met. Prog.*
                             58 (1950) 709.

150. BASINSKI, Z. S. and   The Cubic-Tetragonal Transformation in
     CHRISTIAN, J. W.   Manganese Copper Alloys, *J. Inst.*
                             Metals **80** (1952) 659.

151. JACQUET, P. A.   Micrographic Control of a Refractory
                             Alloy for Turboreactor Blades, (in
                             French), *Rev. Met.* **47** (1950) 568.

152. LORKING, K. F.   The Electropolishing of 'Nimonic 80',
                             Dept. of Supply, Aero. Res. Lab. S.M.
                             Note 205 May (1953); *Trans. Inst. Met.*
                             Finishing **32** (1954–55) 451.

153. LORKING, K. F. and   The Electropolishing of Chromium and
     QUASS, S.   Chromium Base Alloys, *Dept. of*
                             Supply, Aero. Res. Lab. Report Met.
                             No. 3, Oct. (1954).

154. PROSEN, E. M.   Electropolishing of Dental Appliances,
                             U.S. Pat. 2,674,571 (1954); *see also*
     DUFFIELD, P.   Electrolytic Polishing of Chromium-
                             Cobalt Alloys Used in Dentistry, *Brit.*
                             Dental J. **98** (1955) 13.

155. MIYOSHI, A. and   Electrolytic Polishing of Alloys of Tung-
     KURIHARA, I.   sten or Tungsten Carbide, (in Japan-
                          ese), Jap. Pat. 263 (1951); see also
                          SAITO, N. "Electrolyte for Electro-
                          polishing Alloys of the WC-Co and
                          WC-Ti-Co Systems", Jap. Pat. 2959
                          (1952).

156. PELLISIER, G. E.,   Electrolytic Polishing of Metals, Met.
     MARKUS, H. and   Prog. 38 (1940) 554.
     MEHL, R. F.

157. FEDOT'EV, N. P.   Regeneration of Solutions Used in
     KRUGLOVA, E. G. and Electropolishing of Steel, (in Russian),
     GRILIKHES, S. Y.   Zhur. Priklad. Khim. 27 (1954) 157.

158. SPARKS, W. A.   The Electrolytic Polishing of Carbon-
                          Manganese Steels, J. Electrodep. Tech.
                          Sec. 21 (1946) 245.

159. BERGER, P.   Electrolytic Polishing of Brass Pressings,
                          Electrodep. Tech. Soc. Third Int. Conf.
                          on Electrodeposition (Sept. 1947) Paper
                          No. 4. Process is covered by Br. Pat.
                          603,545 (1948).

160. FAUST, C. L.   Electropolishing, Monthly Rev. Am.
                          Electroplaters' Soc. 31 (1944) 807; see
                          also
                          Electropolishing: What is its Status
                          Today? J. Electrodep. Tech. Soc. 21
                          (1946) 181.
     FAUST, C. L. and   Industrial Electropolishing, Proc. Am.
     GRAVES, E. E.   Electroplaters' Soc. 35 (1948) 223.

161. WERNICK, S.   Electrolytic Polishing and Bright Plating
                          of Metals, Alvin Redman Ltd., London
                          (1948).

162. ZENTLER-GORDON, H. E. New Developments of Electrolytic Polish-
                          ing, J. Electrodep. Tech. Soc. 26 (1950)
                          55.

163. CHARLESWORTH, P. A. The Electrochemical Manipulation of
     and HOBSON, C.   Stainless Steels and High Duty Alloys,
                          Sheet Met. Ind. 30 (1953) 825.

164. MONDON, R.   Some Successful Applications of Electro-
                          polishing in Industry, Sheet Met. Ind.
                          32 (1955) 923.

165. MICHEL, P.

Production of Exact Geometrical Forms by Electrolytic Polishing, (in French), *Rev. Met.* **46** (1949) 39.

166. HERENGUEL, J. and SEGOND, R.

Special Light Alloys for Electropolishing and Anodic Oxidation, (in French), *Met. et Corr.* **24** (1949) 45; also *Eng. Digest* **10** (1949) 27.

167. HALUT, R. E.

Technical Applications of Electrolytic Polishing, *Electrodep. Tech. Soc. Third Int. Conf. on Electrodeposition* (*Sept.* 1947) *Paper No.* 2.

168. MONDON, R. and ZENTLER-GORDON, H. E.

Electrolytic Polishing and Metal Fatigue, *Trans. Inst. Met. Finishing* **31** (1954) 52.

169. STEER, A. T., WILSON, J. K. and WRIGHT, O.

Electropolishing: Its Influence on the Fatigue-Endurance Limit of Ferrous and Non-Ferrous Parts, *Aircraft Prod.* **15** (1953) 242.

170. PULLEN, N. D.

An Anodic Treatment for the Production of Aluminium Reflectors, *J. Inst. Metals* **59** (1936) 151. Patents held by British Aluminium Co. are Br. Pat. 449,162 (1936); 513,530 (1939); 523,375 (1940); Fr. Pat. 798,956 (1936); 853,754 (1939); 881,701 (1943); U.S. Pat. 2,339,806 (1944). A modification of the solution using 0·01 to 0·1 per cent sodium octyl sulphate, as an addition agent to prevent pitting attack, has been developed (Br. Pat. 624,483 (1949); Can. Pat. 461,222 (1949).

PULLEN, N. D. and SCOTT, B. A.

Alkaline Electro-Brightening and Anodizing Aluminium, *Trans. Inst. Met. Finishing* **33** (1956) 163.

171. HONEYCOMBE, R. W. K. and TEGART, W. J. McG.

Electrolytic Polishing of Aluminium, *C.S.I.R.* (*Aust.*) *Section of Tribophysics.** *Report B.33* (July) 1947.

* Now C.S.I.R.O. Division of Tribophysics.

132   REFERENCES

172. Aluminum Co. of America.

The Alzak process is the name usually given to the process employing fluoboric acid electrolyte (U.S. Patent 2, 108,603 (1933); Br. Patent 433,484 (1935); 436,154 (1936); 436,381 (1936); 440,827 (1936); 489,169 (1938); Fr. Pat. 773,680 (1934); 778,018 (1935); German Pat. 626,758 (1934)) but two other processes have been patented by this company, one for a sulphuric acid/hydrofluoric acid electrolyte (Fr. Pat. 778,019 (1935); U.S. Pat. 2,040,618 (1936); Can. Pat. 354,511 (1935)) and the other for a chromic acid/hydrofluoric acid electrolyte (Fr. Pat. 778,019 (1935); Can. Pat. 354,510 (1935); U.S. Pat. 2,040,617 (1936)).

173. WERNICK, S. and PINNER, R.

The Surface Treatment and Finishing of Aluminium and Its Alloys, Robert Draper Ltd., London (1956).

174. Battelle Memorial Institute.

A wide range of electrolytes is covered by Brit. Pat. 526,854 (1940); 552,638 (1943); French Pat. 918,756 (1946); 921,342 (1947); U.S. Pat. 2,282,350–1 (1943); 2,550,544 (1951).

175. Battelle Memorial Institute.

Results for several detailed compositions and conditions are tabulated in U.S. Pat. 2,347,039 (1944): 2,366,714 (1945).

176. AXTELL, W. G.

Electropolishing Brass, *Iron Age* **163** June 30 (1950) 48. The process is covered by U.S. Pat. 2,645,611 (1953).

177. HEYES, J.

Das elektrolytische Polieren, Deutscher Fachzeitschriften u. Fachbuch Verlag, Stuttgart (1955).

178. ZMESKAL, O.

Electrolytic Polishing of Stainless Steel and other Metals, *Met. Prog.* **47** (1945) 729.

179. UHLIG, H. H.

The Electrolytic Polishing of Stainless Steels, *Trans. Electrochem. Soc.* **78** (1940) 265.

180. Munitions Supply Laboratories.*

Method for Electropolishing Stainless Steel, *M.S.L. Rep. Met. No.* M45–3015 (1945).

* Now Defence Standards Laboratories (Aust.).

181. Battelle Memorial Institute.

A wide range of orthophosphoric acid/ sulphuric acid electrolytes for various steel compositions have been patented:—U.S. Pat. 2,334,698 (1943); 2,334,699 (1943); 2,338,321 (1944). Such solutions have been modified by increasing the sulphuric acid content and adding glycerine to increase their "covering power" (U.S. Pat. 2,348,577 (1944); Br. Pat. 526,854 (1940)). Pitting attack has also been reduced by the addition of alcohols (U.S. Pat. 2,461,035 (1949); 2,461,036 (1949)).

182. LIPPERT, T. W.

Pickle-Polished Stainless Steel, *Iron Age* **145** (Jan.) (1940) 22. The process is covered by U.S. Pat. 2,331,721 (1943); 2,335,354 (1943); Br. Pat. 529,944 (1940).

183. Battelle Memorial Institute.

A wide range of electrolytes is covered by U.S. Pat. 2,334,699 (1943); Br. Pat. 558,727 (1944).

184. GRAY, D.

Electropolishing Silver in Cyanide Solution, *Proc. Amer. Electroplaters' Soc.* **35** (1948) 241.

185. GRAY, D. and EATON, S. E.

A New Process for Electropolishing Silver, *Iron Age* **159** (Apr. 10) (1947) 64. The process is covered by U.S. Pat. 2,416,294 (1947). This electrolyte is also claimed to polish cadmium and nickel-silver.

186. Battelle Memorial Institute.

The process is covered by U.S. Pat. 2,373,466 (1945).

187. PINNER, R.

Theory and Practice of Chemical Polishing Pt. III. The Theory of Chemical Polishing, *Electroplating* **7** (1954) 127.

188. SODERBERG, G.

Bright Dipping, *Trans. Am. Electrochem. Soc.* **88** (1945) 297.

189. SCHMID, G. and SPAHN, H.

On the Chemical Polishing of Brass and Nickel Silver, (in German), III, *Z. Metallkunde* **46** (1955) 128; IV, *Z. Elektrochem.* **60** (1956) 365.

190. HICKLING, A.,　　　　The Nature of the Film Present on Iron
MARSHALL, W. A.　　　after Brightening in Marshall's Solu-
and BUCKLE, H.　　　　tion, *J. Electrodep. Tech. Soc.* **28**
　　　　　　　　　　　　(1952) 47.

HICKLING, A. and　　　The Chemical Polishing of Mild Steel by
ROSTRON, J.　　　　　Hydrogen Peroxide-Oxalic Acid Mix-
　　　　　　　　　　　　tures, *Trans. Inst. Met. Finishing* **32**
　　　　　　　　　　　　(1954–55) 229.

191. NAPIER, D. H. and　　Anodizing, *Met. Ind.* **76** (7) (1950) 123.
WESTWOOD, J. V.

192. BEAUJARD, L.　　　　Chemical Polishing of Iron and Mild
　　　　　　　　　　　　Steel, (in French), *C. R. Acad. Sci.*
　　　　　　　　　　　　(Paris) **234** (1952) 440.

193. HERENGUEL, J. and　　Chemical Polishing of Aluminium and
SEGOND, R.　　　　　its Alloys, (in French), *Rev. Met.* **48**
　　　　　　　　　　　　(1951) 262.

194. HERENGUEL, J.　　　Chemical Polishing of Aluminium and
　　　　　　　　　　　　its Alloys, (in French), *Rev. Aluminium*
　　　　　　　　　　　　30 (1953) 261.

195. BEACH, J. G. and　　Electroplating on Beryllium, *J. Electro-*
FAUST, C. L.　　　　*chem. Soc.* **100** (1953) 276.

196. MCAFEE, J.　　　　The Polishing and Etching of Metals,
　　　　　　　　　　　　Aust. Inst. Met., Symposium on "Recent
　　　　　　　　　　　　Advances in Physical Metallurgy. Part
　　　　　　　　　　　　I. *Metallography*" (1944); *Aust. Eng.*
　　　　　　　　　　　　Year Book (1944).

197. DE JONG, J. J.　　　Chemical Polishing of Metals and Alloys,
　　　　　　　　　　　　(in Dutch), *Metalen* **9** (1954) 2.

198. GREINER, E. S.　　　Plastic Deformation of Germanium and
　　　　　　　　　　　　Silicon by Torsion, *Trans. A.I.M.E.*
　　　　　　　　　　　　203 (1955) 204; *J. Metals* **7** (1955) 204.

199. WORNER, H. K. and　　The Preparation of Lead and Lead-Rich
WORNER, H. W.　　　Alloys for Microscopic Examination,
　　　　　　　　　　　　J. Inst. Metals **66** (1940) 45.

200. EDWARDS, A. R. and　　Polishing and Etching Magnesium in
HANNA, K. R.　　　　Nitric Acid, *Aust. Eng.* Nov. 8 (1948)
　　　　　　　　　　　　37.

201. GRAHAM, L. W.,　　　Preparation of Steel Specimens for
CRANSTON, J. P. and　　Micro-Examination by a Chemical
AXON, H. J.　　　　　Polishing Technique, "Research Corre-
　　　　　　　　　　　　spondence S20", issued with *Research*
　　　　　　　　　　　　8, (1955).

202. MARSHALL, W. A.   A Non-Electrolytic Smoothing Treatment for Steel, *J. Electrodep. Tech. Soc.* **28** (1952) 27. Patent application No. 16578/51.

SACHS, K. and ODGERS, M.   Smoothing of Mild Steel by Barrel Treatment in Oxalic Acid–Hydrogen Peroxide Solution, *Trans. Inst. Met. Finishing* **33** (1956).

203. VERMILYEA, D. A.   The Kinetics of Formation and Structure of Anodic Oxide Films on Tantalum, *Acta Met.* **1** (1953) 282.

204. CAIN, F. M.   *Zirconium and Zirconium Alloys*, Am. Soc. Metals, Cleveland (1953) 176.

205. BRACE, A. W.   The Electrolytic and Chemical Polishing and Brightening of Aluminium and Its Alloys, *Met. Finishing J.* **1** (1955) 253, 319.

206. GARDAM, G. E. and PEEK, R.   Studies in Bright Anodising by the Ammonium Bifluoride–Nitric Acid Process, *Trans. Inst. Met. Finishing* **33** (1956) 198.

BAUMANN, F. and NEUNZIG, H.   Chemically Brightening and Anodising Aluminium and Its Alloys for Use in Automobile Manufacture, *Trans. Inst. Met. Finishing* **33** (1956) 211.

The "Erftwerk" process is covered by Brit. Pat. 693,776 and 693,876 (1950). Similar solutions have been patented by Kaiser Aluminium and Chemical Corp. [U.S. Pat. 2,593,447–8–9 (1949); 2,620,265 and 2,640,806 (1951)] and General Motors Corp. [U.S. Pat. 2,614,913 (1950) and 2,625,468 (1951)].

207. SODERBERG, G.   Discolouration of Cadmium Plate and its Prevention, *Trans. Am. Electrochem. Soc.* **62** (1932) 39. The processes are covered by the following patents: U.S. 2,021,592 (1935); 2,186,479 (1940); 2,194,498 (1940).

208. E. I. DUPONT DE NEMOURS and CO.   U.S. Patents are assigned to: KEPFER, R. J. 2,154,455 (1939); HULL, R. O. 2,154,451 (1939); OPLINGER, F. L. 2,154,468 (1939;) 2,154,469 (1939).

136   REFERENCES

209. PINNER, R.   Theory and Practice of Chemical Polishing. Pt. I. Chemical Processes for Copper-Base Alloys, *Electroplating* **6** (1953) 360.

210. Battelle Memorial Institute.   The process is covered by: U.S. Pat. 2,446,040 (1948).

211. SCHMID, G. and SPAHN, H.   On the Chemical Polishing of Brass and Nickel-Silver. I and II, (in German), *Z. Metallkunde* **45** (1954) 392 and 398.

212. BROUILLET, P., EPELBOIN, I. and FROMENT, M.   Determination of the Valence of Metallic Ions during Polishing in the Presence of ClO_4^- Ions, (in French), *C. R. Acad. Sci. (Paris)* **239** (1954) 1795.

EPELBOIN, I.   Contribution to the Study of Anodic Phenomena During Electrolytic Dissolution of Metals, (in French), *Z. Elektrochem.* **59** (1955) 689.

213. STRAUMANIS, M. E.   Uncommon Valency Ions and the Difference Effect, *J. Electrochem. Soc.* **105** (1958) 284.

214. VINAVER, W. and DRUELLE, P.   The Phenomenon of Migration of the Zinc–Lead Eutectic in Cast Zinc, (in French), *Rev. Met.* **52** (1955) 612.

215. Anon.   Methods for Determination of Sulphuric and Phosphoric Acids in Electropolishing Solutions, *Plating Notes (D.R.L. Aust.)* **2** (4) (1950) 128.

INDEX